The Short Story Series

GENERAL EDITOR   JAMES GIBSON

LOVE
SUPERNATURAL
DETECTION
HORROR
SCIENCE FICTION
HUMOUR

Love

CHOSEN BY

Helen Morris

John Murray

Albemarle Street London

Printed and bound in Great Britain
by Butler & Tanner Ltd,
Frome and London

0 7195 3504 2

CONTENTS

Walter Macken

The Coll Doll

I was at a loose end this Monday morning in March, see. I get up in the morning all right. I have my breakfast, ready to go to work, but there is no work to go to since I was sacked on Saturday but I haven't passed on this item of information to my father and mother. There are eleven of us in the house including them, and you have to shout all the time to make yourself heard. It was that foreman. He didn't like me. I like to be clean and well turned out. That is my own business. Even if you work in a factory you don't have to look like a coal heaver all the time. I liked clean working clothes, and I liked to keep my hair well. This was my own business.

But this fellow sneered a lot at me, 'Brilliantine Boy', he would say and 'The Scabby Gent'. He was a big burly fellow and I took a lot from him. I don't think he meant to be nasty. He was just a big stupid, half-human ape.

I am nineteen, so on Saturday I clonked him with a spade handle. I know I shouldn't have done this. It didn't do much damage to his skull, which is as thick as his intellect, but I had no case, and nobody wept when I got my cards.

It's hard to tell your people a thing like this. All they see is that the money coming into the house is short. They don't see that a man, even if he is only nineteen, is entitled to his dignity, and entitled to defend it.

I like my oul fella, you know. He's all right. He just works, and comes home and washes and goes out to his pub and spends the night over a few pints with his friends. He'll clout you one or maybe two, but he mainly roars at us to keep us quiet. My mother is all right too, but looking after a houseful, after giving birth to them, and losing a few on the way, doesn't give her time to sit down by the fire and talk over your frustrations. You see what I mean?

I didn't like working in factories. I got a scholarship from the primary school and went on for a few years to a secondary school, but I had to quit and go to work. The money was needed at home.

There's no use giving fellows like me a scholarship if they won't give the parents a sort of scholarship too, to make up for the loss of probable wages.

So I wasn't even half educated in a way. I tried to make up for this by eating books from the County Library, but you feel you are reading without direction. Your mind is going so many places at once that it is too much for it. It is like sucking the sea through a straw, see. My pals call me Schol, and pretend to defer to my knowledge, but this is just for laughs. I know myself how limited my knowledge is, and I long for it, but at the present I see no way, no way at all. All those young ones coming up after me that have to be fed and clothed on what my father earns and what I earn, or rather what I don't earn now.

So I walked, out into the country. I thought I'd take in a bit of this nature stuff, just to pass the time. It's not done, you know. Maybe on account of the tight shoes we all wear these days. All right for show and dancing, but you rarely use them to walk, just up and down the streets of the town, and you can't call that walking.

It was a bright sunny day. The sea looked happy, grinning away in the sunbeams. The hills across the bay were misted and coloured. It was odd to be walking the promenade on a Monday morning. Just a few old ladies going to Mass in the Church and elderly fellows, past working, walking dogs or sitting on the seats smoking pipes.

I felt guilty, see, uneasy. I should be at work, earning money, not strolling on the prom on a Monday morning. To hell with it. I jumped down on the sand, and threw a few stones at the sea. Farther on I got flat stones and started skimming them on the calm water, seeing how many hops I could get in. The best was eleven before the stone sank.

Then I felt that the walkers' eyes were on me, saying: What is a young fellow like that doing on the sand on a Monday morning? Why isn't he working, or emigrating? One look at me and the way I was dressed, my whole appearance, and they would know I wasn't the son of a moneyed gent.

So I went away from there, seeking loneliness; even the windows of the houses and hotels seemed like accusing eyes to me. I left the promenade and walked on the winding road that left the sea and ran up and down the hill: past small rivers and down in a hollow through a wood. I leaned on the bridge here for a little while, looking at the clear water running over washed stones. I could see a shelter in the woods there, a glade that was stabbed with sunbeams shining through the branches. I thought it might be nice to go in there and lie on the grass, and stay forever, just listening to the sound of the water, but then a large red cow, one of these walking milk bottles came right into the middle of the glade and dropped a card, plop, plop, plop, ruining everything, see, like life, so I laughed and left.

My shoes were hurting me now. I had to stop and wriggle my toes to ease them. I was sorry I wasn't younger, like years ago when you could go in your bare feet, until the soles became as tough as leather. That was necessity. Now young people would rather be seen dead than in their bare feet. I suppose this was progress too. Here I was, thinking like I was a hundred years old.

I saw this sandy lane, so I turned down it. It looked a lonely lane, deep cart-wheel tracks on it, and dry stone walls each side of it, and it was aimed in a crooked way at the sea. This was for me. The sand was soft on the feet.

It opened out into a rock-strewn beach at the sea. There was a brave smell there, of healthy things, and seaweed. There was a sandy beach as well, and at the far end a cliff rising straight up, like the back of it was covered with a green carpet. There were sheep grazing on it. Now that's the place for me, I thought, and headed for it.

I was halfway towards it, walking on the sand, thinking: Well there's no one here but me and the birds, when a girl suddenly came from the shelter of these rocks and almost ran into me. She had been behind a rock taking off her shoes and stockings I would say, and then turned for a run on the sand.

'Oh,' she said, startled. 'I'm sorry.'

Her feet were very small and nearly as pale as the sand.

I saw fear in her face as she looked at me. All right, I was an odd fellow to see at this time and place. What did she think I was going to do? Jump on her straight away without even an introduction and rape her? She was a nice little thing, maybe seventeen or so. That's what I say, she reminded me of one of those colleen dolls you see in boxes in shop windows. She was dark and had a round face, and wide blue eyes with thick dark lashes. She was wearing a wide skirt that was like the leaves of a melodeon, a white blouse and a black cardigan affair. I took all this in. I was going to make a snide remark, because I was angry at the fear in her face, but I didn't. I said: 'Sorry, miss' and walked past her without another look and headed for the cliff. I was thinking: How quick people are to look at you and assess you, from your accent and your clothes and put you into a box marked Dangerous, or Inferior. Without even talking to you!

I was about five minutes getting to the top of the cliff, and I stretched myself there looking at the white clouds in the blue sky.

Maybe I just gave up and drifted off to sleep. Anyhow I heard a scream. At first I thought it was a sea bird since sometimes they can cry like children. Then I sat up and turned my head and looked down at the strand. This girl was sitting down, holding her foot, and even from here I could see the scarlet of blood against the white sand. So she cut her foot, I thought. That's fine, and I went to lay back again, but she was looking straight up at me, and I couldn't do it. I got up and ran down the cliff, leaped the fence at the end and jumped down on the sand.

Her face was white. She was holding the bloody sole of her foot with small hands, and her fingers were scarlet.

I got on my knees and took the foot in my hand. It was badly gashed. I squeezed the edges of it and closed the wound. 'What happened?' I asked.

'I stood on a broken bottle,' she said. 'Isn't it very bad?'

She was afraid now all right, but it was different fear from the other. It would take three stitches to close it, I thought.

'It's not too bad,' I said. 'It looks worse than it is. One stitch should close it.'

'Will I bleed to death?' she asked.

I felt like patting her head. 'No, no,' I said. 'No fear of that. Let me lift you down to the water and we'll wash it.'

I put my arms under her. She wasn't very heavy. She made no protest. I carried her to the water's edge. We left a trail of blood on the sand.

I put her down there and took a clean handkerchief, and, finding sand-free water, I washed out the wound. It was a jagged gash and it was bleeding freely, which was good. I gave her the wet handkerchief.

'Wash the blood off your hands with this,' I said. She did so. She was still very pale, and she was trembling. 'Have you never been cut before?' I asked.

'Oh, no,' she said. 'Just thorn cuts.'

'It's not as bad as you think it is,' I said. 'But we'll have to get up the main road and try and get a lift to the hospital.'

'You are awful kind,' she said.

I took the handkerchief and washed it in the sea, and then I tied it very tightly around her foot. I hurt her, because she gasped, but it had to be tight. 'Where are your shoes and things?' I asked.

'Behind that rock,' she said, pointing. I left her and went over there. Small shoes with the stockings rolled and pushed into them. I took those and put them, one each, in my coat pocket and went back to her.

'I will have to carry you now.' I said.

'Amn't I very heavy?' she asked.

I lifted her easily. 'Hold on to my neck,' I said. She put her arms around my neck and it eased the burden. 'I'll tell you the story of the King,' I said. You know this story about a King who was a great hunter and wanted to be praised, but a female of the court said that anyone could do anything with a lot of practice. So he was annoyed and ordered the forester to kill her. The forester didn't kill her, but kept her in his house in the woods. There was an outside staircase and each day she would take a small calf, put him on her shoulders and carry him up and down these stairs. He became bigger and bigger until the calf was a great big bullock, but by dint of practice she could carry the huge beast up and down the stairs. One day the King came and saw this and learned his lesson.

'What? Am I a cow?' she asked. I laughed. Some of the paleness was leaving her face.

'No,' I said. 'It just shows you.'

'Are you often carrying girls like this?' she asked.

'Not often,' I said. 'You are the first.'

'You are not afraid of blood and cuts?' she asked.

'I got fourteen stitches in my right leg,' I said.

'How?' she asked.

'A machine that went wrong,' I said. 'But that's nothing. I know a man in our street with forty-eight stitches.'

'Forty-eight!' she exclaimed.

I didn't say that he got the stitches as the result of a sort of bottle party, a broken-bottle party.

'That's right,' I said. 'So one stitch in the sole of your foot won't seem too bad.'

'Oh, no,' she said. 'I was afraid I was going to die. Isn't that silly? Wasn't I lucky you were there?'

Listen, I want to tell you something. This was the best time of my life since the day I was born. I made her laugh. I made her forget her cut, which must be paining now. I told her funny things about my young sister and my brothers, the things they got up to. She had no sisters or brothers and I felt one with her. I was carrying her in my arms. I could feel all the softness of her, her breath on the side of my cheek, her soft hair brushing against my forehead; it wasn't those things, it was just that the two of us were one person, like, going up that road. It was like the fulfilment of a day-dream, if you know what I mean. She liked me, I was just me and she was just a part of me like an arm or a leg or a heart. Do you know what I mean? I thought that all things are destined, marked out to happen just like the rising and the setting of the sun. Now I could see a reason for why I was sacked, and why I walked the lonely places looking for something, searching. And I had found it. I felt that I was walking a foot above the ground. How many times in life has that happened to you?

It stayed with me. We got a lift in the first car that passed, an oldish man with a black moustache and a bald head. She was a pretty girl, of course. I would have been waiting by the side of the road for a lift until I grew whiskers, or a tinker's van would pass by. All this didn't matter. She wanted me with her, see. She got comfort for my presence. She held on to my hand and I rested her foot on my knee.

Even at the hospital she wouldn't let me go. I had to go in with her to the room where they fix up people. I knew it well, since I was a boy. It was practically a second home for us with cuts and bruises and fellows swallowing spoons and bones and things.

I held her hand while they gave her this tetanus injection and while they stitched the cut and bandaged it. Then I said, 'You wait here now until I arrange for a hackney to take you home.'

'Don't be long,' she said. 'Please come back.'

She did. She said this.

I went outside the place. Turk was just swinging away having dropped a client, so I whistled him and he came back when he heard the beryl.

'What's up, Schol?' he asked. 'What's the game? I'd know your whistle a mile away.'

'No back-chat, cabby,' I said. 'Just stick around. I'm bringing out a client.'

'Yeah,' he said, 'and who pays? Any client of yours is a free ride.'

I went down to him. I had a fistful of coins.

'Take your filthy lucre out of that, Scrooge,' I said.

He looked at the money. 'So you can pay,' he said. 'All right. I'll trust you.'

I went back then again to her.

Now I didn't have to carry her. She was wearing one shoe on her good foot and they had a wheel chair to bring her along the corridor and out to the steps. But I carried her from there to the hackney. Turk was so surprised that he even got his great bulk out of the car and opened the back door. I put her in the seat and got in beside her. She kept holding my hand.

'Where to, Miss?' Turk asked her. I was glad to see that he could see that she was a lady and treated her with respect. Otherwise he would have said something coarse. She told him where to go.

She was looking at me.

'It's all over now,' I said. 'It wasn't too bad, eh?'

'No,' she said. 'How will I ever thank you for all you have done for me?'

I didn't know how to answer that. I just swallowed my adam's apple. I don't do that often. You see, ever since it had happened, all that time she was so close to me, I had felt no evil in me. Do you know what I mean? It was all part of the clean and beautiful things of life. I know this sounds odd, blood and gaping cuts and hospitals and disinfectant, but it was so. And it wasn't just a dream, either. It was as real as life.

It seemed to me a very short time before the car went in through open iron gates and up a short winding drive. There was a house with steps leading up to it, a fine big house with lots of windows. I took her out of the car and carried her up the steps to the door. And this burst open and a very well dressed white-haired woman came out and a maid with a black dress and a small white apron.

And the woman said: 'My God! What happened? What in the name of God happened to you?'

And the girl said: 'I was on the beach and I cut my foot on a bottle and he was marvellous to me. He got me to the hospital and brought me home.'

'My dear! My dear!' said her mother, taking and embracing her, and then looking at me over her shoulder. Looking at me up and down and she said: 'We are very grateful to you. Julia, go in and bring out my purse.'

The girl said in horror: 'Mother!' but it was too late, see, the bubble was burst.

I still had her other shoe and stocking in my pocket. I took it out and put it in the mother's hand, and then I turned and went down the steps and into the car beside Turk, and shouted at him: 'Get out of here!' and he shifted gears and left.

I could hear voices saying: 'No! No! Come back! Please come back!' but what was the use? The blindfold was down. I saw myself in her mother's eyes. Reach for the purse. A cobweb can be shattered by a stick, a big one, totally destroyed, and the spider can come along afterwards and fix it. But we are not spiders. We may be very dumb but we can see a thing when it is in front of our nose. I felt as if I had suffered a bad beating. I had been beaten before in fights, but never knocked out. I was like that now, as if I was knocked out, see.

I don't remember much after that.

We were in a pub. It was late, I think. Other men were there and Turk. And I heard Turk talking. He was saying about Schol having a doll down on the beach, a real doll. Turk's coll doll, a real smashing doll, and what he wanted to know was had Schol tumbled her on the sand.

So I hit him. And Turk hit me, and somebody else hit me, and I hit him. And later the blues were there and I hit them and they hit me with a truncheon. I fought and struck out.

Now I know I am in the lazer in the back of the police place. I am not drunk. I am sick. But I am not sick in the way that they think. I am heart sick, heart sick. So I take this stool and I start banging the door with it, so that maybe they will have to come and quieten me some more. This is what I want. Because I can tell nobody, see. It will be with me forever. It could never be, unless I was born different and she was born different. But I can't forget, and I feel a fire eating away at my chest. And there is nobody I can tell. Nobody at all. Nobody in the wide world. Who would understand? Who would know? Who would believe?

A Question of Background

I wanted you to be the first to hear about it, Gladys; because it's all due to you, really, that it came about. If it hadn't been for you suddenly giving me backword, and going off to Blackpool with Jack Hepworth and his sister, instead of coming to the Isle of Man with me as we'd arranged, I should never have met him. Or if I had, I shouldn't have—well, never mind; I'll begin at the beginning.

You know, I always hated Hudley, Gladys. I hated the West Riding altogether; the towns so dark and dreary; the great blocks of dingy mills; the steep, narrow, dirty streets; the foundry furnaces and the mill chimneys; the noisy trams and buzzers; and the great smoke cloud over all. I hated the lorries always thundering about, because they never seemed to carry anything thrilling or romantic, like ivory or apes or peacocks; they always carried something textile. Dirty fleeces; or those yarn tops whose coils look so nice and white but are so greasy to touch; or pieces of cloth, flopping about on their way to the dyers; or something dull like that. I always hated the mills, and made up my mind I'd never have anything to do with them, and so I worked hard at school, and got a scholarship to the technical college, and worked hard there and got very good certificates for shorthand and book-keeping and typing, and meant to go away and work at some interesting, romantic place. And then poor old dad went and asked Mr Sykes if there was a place for me in the office at Haighroyd Mills, and Mr Sykes said there was, and I had to go or break dad's heart, and so of course I went.

But I grew to hate everything to do with cloth more and more, because things were always going wrong. Mr Robert or Mr John was always rushing into the office wanting to know where piece 85431 or something was, because some customer wanted it urgently, or the customer himself came on the telephone in a rage; and then someone was always shouting at me: 'Bessie! Just 'phone round and see if you can find piece 85431,' and there I was at the house-'phone half the morning, arguing with the foremen of the departments about a missing piece. At first I used to be timid about it, and the piece never turned up because they didn't bother to look, and Mr Robert used to fly into a fury and rush off down into the mill and blow up everybody he met till the whole place seethed with irritation—yes, the whole fifteen acres of it. But after a while I hardened my heart and stood no nonsense from any of them; no, not from my father himself in the warehouse, nor that cheeky fellow on the big tentering machine, nor that tiresome, slow man in the press-shop, nor any of them. I knew all their names and how best to stir them up, though I wouldn't demean myself by knowing any of them personally, except dad, of course. Not that it was much good when I *did* find the piece Mr Robert was after; there was usually something wrong with it: the finish wasn't right, or the length was wrong, or it had got damaged in the weave, or something. Oh, yes, I simply hated everything to do with textiles.

And that was why I was so determined not to go for the Wakes to Douglas or Blackpool, where everybody from Hudley goes; I wanted to go to a nice quiet place where I should meet some fresh people. I wanted to go down south really, but mother wouldn't let me go alone, and when you said you'd go to Port Erin and showed me those picture postcards—however, you know all about that. And then you gave me backword and we arranged I should go alone and not tell mother.

Well, Port Erin is the loveliest, most romantic place I've ever been in. There's a little bay, sheltered on one side by some low cliffs and on the other by Bradda Head. Bradda Head is simply glorious! At the top it's all purple heather, with sheep grazing, though the sides are so steep you'd think they'd roll off; then there are huge rugged black rocks going sheer down into the sea, where the seagulls live. Those gulls! I could watch them for hours. They're always swirling and swooping up and down, except on hot afternoons, when they stand very still and dig into their feathers with their curved beaks. The sea at Port Erin is very, very clear, and beautifully blue; on a sunny morning it sparkles so you can hardly see it for light. The houses are coloured pink and white, the shore is nice firm honey-coloured sand, and there's a little harbour, with a few fishing-smacks, and lots of little rowing-boats, brown and white, tied to each other in long strings or dotted about the bay.

But the best part of Port Erin is the breakwater. It seems that they built it out at the wrong angle from the land, and the first storm that came, wrecked it. So now it looks like a pier only for a few yards, and then turns into a jumble of concrete blocks, as if a child had upset a box of bricks. There's all kinds of seaweed—ribbed and flat and curly and some like rope—gently swaying about there in the tide; and there are fat, red anemones, like velvet, and round, prickly sea-urchins, all lovely pinks and purples, clinging to the rocks below, and the water's so clear that you can see them, oh! ever so far down; and in some of the shallow places there are tiny darting fish and little green crabs and lobsters, all transparent, waving their pretty little feelers. Oh, it's a lovely place; I used to spend hours there, just looking about and feeling happy, and thinking how different it was from Hudley and how glad I was to be there.

It was there I met him. I had scrambled out to one of the blocks and was sitting there, looking about and thinking, like I said, when suddenly I heard a voice saying: 'Excuse me.'

I looked round, and there was a young man in a rowing boat, quite near my rock. He looked a nice, decent sort of fellow, not the kind who go about picking up strange girls, but all the same I gave him rather a haughty stare, being alone.

'Get in,' he said, and drew his boat up close to me.

I thought this was rude, so I scrambled up, meaning to go back to land and leave him, when I saw that I was quite cut off by the tide. Between my rock and the next there was a stretch of deep water, full of floating seaweed, with no safe footholds to be seen, and as I stood gazing the water swirled ...

I felt so dizzy and queer, I gave a scream; and of course I slipped, and my arms and legs flew in all directions, you know how they do, and there was an awful moment when I didn't know whether I was in the sea or out, and suddenly I found myself in the boat, quite safe except for bruises on my arm where he'd clutched me, and he was looking at me in a concerned way, and some people on the land were shouting and laughing. I felt ashamed of myself for being so silly and causing such a fuss, and I hoped he wouldn't put me ashore where all the people were; and without my saying a word he understood, and turned the boat round very cleverly, and rowed away down the middle of the bay.

Well, it's no use going into what I said to him and what he said to me. Not that he said much; looking back, I see it was me did all the talking. You either like a person or you don't, and you can never make somebody else understand why. He was tall, and broad, and strong, and dark, and rather dreamy, quiet and serious, you know, not always making silly jokes like fellows in the West Riding; he could row and swim and walk, champion, and we liked the same things, always.

It was the Wednesday of Wakes week I met him, and after that we were together all the time. We rowed all round Bradda Head and into the caves, that afternoon, and I said it was grand, and very different from Hudley, and he said there were caves like that in Cornwall, and I thought how grand it would be to live in Cornwall. Next day it was rough in the morning and we stood on the breakwater and watched the waves; how huge they were, and green, and my word, the white spray! You don't see anything like that in Hudley. In the afternoon, as it was too rough for boating, we went for a walk; there were little white cottages, and fuchsias by the door, and fields of golden barley all rustling, and poppies, and cliffs, and an old castle; and I said how different it was from Hudley, and how I liked it. The next day it was calm and fine again, and we rowed out to the Calf of Man! Yes, we did really, and it was lovely. Heather and rocks and a wide, clear sky. Very different from Hudley, as I said. That night we went down to the breakwater together, and the moon was out; everything was black and silver, very lovely and romantic, and I couldn't bear to think that next day I had to go back to Hudley, and never see him again. He'd never asked my name, and so I didn't like to ask his; to myself I called him Gerald, because that was always my favourite name for a man, so refined and romantic. But if you don't know a person's real name, you never see them again, do you? So it was rather sadly that I said, as we were walking back:

'I'm going home tomorrow.'

And he said: 'So am I.'

So then I felt a little better, because, though I didn't know where he lived, I thought it quite likely he might be crossing to Liverpool, and we should do so much travelling together.

And so it turned out. We both caught the early morning train— you've no idea how those little Manx trains go pottering along between the fuchsias, Gladys; but I didn't care how long it pottered, the longer the better while I was with him. At Douglas it was all so exciting, with the crowds and the steamers with their coloured funnels, and Gerald was splendid; we got on the boat in no time, and he found good places on the deck, not on the smoky side. It was a lovely crossing; the sun shone, and the sky and the sea were very blue. All too soon for me seagulls screamed and flew about, showing that land was near; and then we sighted it, and then we passed the Mersey lightship, with that dismal clanking bell, and crossed the bar into the river, and the water lost its beautiful blue colour and turned yellow, and then the landing stage appeared. I was so miserable I could have cried; here we were going to part in a few minutes, and he'd never asked my name! The ship turned round and backed into its berth, and those big ropes were thrown ashore and drawn tight, and the gangways rattled down, and everybody made a rush for the shore. Gerald picked up my suitcase as well as his own, and said:

'Take my arm.'

I took it; and we got off the boat splendidly and caught a bus.

I was in such a fluster, catching this bus, that I never thought to wonder whether he really needed to go to Exchange Station or was coming for my sake; but when we were inside the station, and saw one of those big indicators, saying: MANCHESTER, ROCHDALE, TODMORDEN, HUDLEY, my heart sank again. But he went straight ahead to the platform, and found a seat for me, although the train was crammed.

'No change at Manchester,' he said.

'You don't go as far as Manchester?' I said, polite like.

He said never a word, only looked at me; then got into the compartment himself.

I felt a bit worried; surely he didn't think I meant to ask him to come with me! But no, I thought, looking at him again, he isn't that kind of man at all.

Well, we reached Manchester, and he didn't stir; and we went all through Lancashire, and he didn't stir; and we ran through the Summit tunnel, and still he didn't stir; and then we came out into Yorkshire, and there he still was.

By this time I was so miserable I could hardly hold up my head. I felt most uncomfortable about him being there, and yet I couldn't bear the thought of leaving him at Hudley. And we drew nearer and nearer; and there were the same old hills all bundled up together, and the same narrow, winding valleys, and the dark stone walls and the scrubby trees all beaten one way by the wind, and the dirty white hens, and the mill chimneys growing thicker and thicker as we went on. And then at last Hudley Bank came in sight, and the train crossed the viaduct and puffed up the cutting, and ran past the weaving sheds and drew up in Hudley station.

I opened the door myself and jumped out quickly, for I felt I couldn't bear the parting, and wanted to get it over as soon as I could. So I put on a bright smile and swung round, ready to take my case and say good-bye and thank you. And there he was, standing beside me on the platform, with our two cases at his feet.

'What are you getting out here for?' I asked. I spoke pretty sharply, for I wasn't standing any nonsense, you know. And he said—what do you think he said?—he said:

'I live here.'

'*You* live *here*! In *Hudley*!' I said.

'Aye,' he said. 'I work at Sykes's, same as you do. I didn't pick out till this morning that you didn't know me; I owned *you* soon as ever I heard your voice. I'm Albert Cockroft, you know,' he said, 'from the pressing.'

Albert Cockroft! The slow man in the press-shop! And such a West Riding name! I could have cried.

'I'm sorry you don't like Hudley, Bessie,' he went on, very serious, 'for I reckon I shall always have to live here.'

Well! I don't know how to explain it, Gladys, but somehow suddenly everything seemed different. Of course Hudley *is* dirty, and smoky, and ugly, and lots of things it shouldn't be; oh! there's lots of things wrong with Hudley. But somehow all of a sudden I didn't want to run away from it any more; I felt as though I loved it somehow. I wanted to stay in it and do things for it; I wanted to change it, I wanted to make it grand. So I said:

'Don't talk so soft, Albert Cockroft,' I said.

You know, Gladys, I never use those Yorkshire expressions, I don't like them; but I felt I had to be Yorkshire just that once. It was now or never with Albert, and I meant it to be now. So I said: 'Don't talk so soft, Albert Cockroft,' I said. 'Don't you know a joke when you see one? What's wrong with Hudley, anyway?' I said. 'Doesn't it make the finest cloth in the world?'

'So they say,' said Albert, but he still seemed down.

'Well, then!' I said. 'And you help to make it, don't you?'

You never saw such a change in a man's face, never.

'If that's how you look at it, Bessie,' he said, 'I shan't be sorry I took you off that rock.'

'That's how I look at it, Albert Cockroft,' I said.

Well, he didn't say anything, but he just looked at me, and I looked at him, and it was all settled between us, and I knew we should be wed.

And then he picked up our two cases, and we got out of the station, and began to walk up the hill. I looked across the valley and picked out Sykes's chimney, and there was a thin wisp of smoke just beginning to curl up out of it; and I knew the boiler tenterer had got back from his Wakes, and was starting up his fires ready for Monday morning. And do you know, Gladys, when I saw that smoke, I felt that happy, tears came into my eyes. It seemed so exciting somehow, so romantic ...

Bill Naughton

Spiv in Love

She was a bit of a drip was old Myra, but absolutely gone on me. If she hadn't have been I don't suppose I'd have looked on the same side of the street she was on, let alone take her out. But I'm like that I am. I can't turn my back on a woman who looks up to me and thinks I am somebody, even if, what you might say, I can't bear the sight of her otherwise. I must admit a bit of the old flannel goes a long way with me, especially if a woman tells me I dress well. I do like anything like that. Another thing I've got to have is a woman around that I can be off-hand with, blow my top with if I feel like it, and generally say what I want to, clean or dirty. Most women won't stand for it, because they ain't got the savvy to see it don't matter, and that once you've said what you want and done what you want, all the best what was underneath is on top. But them dames that can see it can make a bloke feel at home. Not that I like to go regular with that sort of woman— because as a rule they're on the scruffy side, and a bloke can't show 'em off to his mates in the dance hall or in the pubs, which I like to do with a woman—but if they ain't good enough for a steady, I do like to have one on the side as a fill-in.

Although I say it myself as shouldn't, I was dead smart when I first picked up Myra. I'd a coronation-blue suit at the time, double-breasted, with a pair of dead wide sloping shoulders, and lapels that had piped seams what looked like hand-stitched; suede shoes what looked like real buck-skin, coming up a nice shade of London-brown, a Tortilla collar and shirt (they were just coming in again at the time), and I'd nicked a bit out of the back of the collar and stitched it together again, so that it gave the front points a nice spivvy cutaway look. Best of all was my hat, a trilby, gun-smoke-blue, a good three-quarters of an inch off the brim the whole way round, I'd cut it off, I mean, then pressed it down with a hot iron and damp cloth, so that it had come up with a smashing curl what you wouldn't know but I'd paid thirty bob for it in Charing Cross Road. And thirty bob would have been a lot for a hat in them days.

To give you an idea of how I felt about that little gunsmoke-blue, there was one night I got drawn into a rough-house with the Hammersmith gang, and when it was all over my mate looks at me under a lamp-post: 'Strewth,' he says, 'y'oughter see your eye!' 'Never mind the eye,' I says, 'where's my bleedin' titfer?' And I picks it up out of the gutter only to find that one of the Hammersmith hounds had put his foot right through the crown. I sat on the kerb and fair wept I did when I saw it. I don't object to knife fights, knuckle-dusters, or bicycle chains come to that, but I object to having my clothes spoilt.

But to get back to Myra. It was a fluke on her part that she ever struck up with me at all. Eunice, I had a girl went by the name of Eunice at the time, and she was as different as chalk from Myra. Eunice was my steady, and a real classy dresser.

Now this night I have in mind Eunice wanted to go and see a film I didn't want to see. Come to anything like that and this Eunice could be dead mulish. She wouldn't go and see the film I wanted to see. I can't stand women who want all their own way. So I said to her: 'If that's the way you want it you can hop off this minute,' or words to that effect.

As luck would have it a 37 bus hove in sight as I spoke, and before either of us had time to change our minds she was on it and the conductor had rung the bell. I watched it out of sight, and said what I thought to the back of it.

'Eh?' said somebody at my elbow.

I looked round: 'Hello, Myra,' I knew her by name and sight in the dance hall. 'Where you off?'

'Nowhere in partic,' she said.

'Fancy the Troc?' I said. 'It's a gangster film.'

'I don't mind,' she said.

'It's on me,' I said.

'That's good of you,' she said.

It wasn't what she said, it was the way she looked at me that started it. I could see she was thinking she'd struck lucky at last. And in a way she had. She was dead flattered. But same as I say, she was only a drip, and I'd no intention of sticking it with her. And as the weeks went by, I kept telling her as much.

'I'm only passing my time on,' I'd tell her when we were separating at night and she was mentioning arrangements, 'until summink better comes along.'

'Alright, alright, you've told me a dozen bleedin' times,' she'd say. She wasn't a bit refined when she was needled.

'Well, I want you to keep it in mind, see,' I'd say. I wanted her to understand I didn't want her to get any big ideas so far as I was concerned.

Then like as not she'd say, 'What kind of collar do you want me to cut out for you on your next shirt?'

Myra was handy with scissors and needle and thread, and she'd made a few special collars to my fancy. She knew she could always get round me with anything of that kind. So then we'd start talking about the exact specifications of my next collar, cutaway or points and so on. I love talking about clothes I do.

Now though I was having it off with Myra it did seem to me I was missing something, being as I could do better for myself. Myra wasn't the sort you could show off anywhere. So I'd been telling myself that I'd have to get back with Eunice. As luck would have it I bumped into her at New Cross one Saturday dinner time, and within five minutes we'd fixed it all up again. I took her to the pictures that very same night, but when I'd seen her home, I nipped off—just out of curiosity—nothing else—round to the old dance hall to see if I could catch Myra going off with a bloke. As it happened, she was on her own; so I took her off to tell her it was all over.

'That's the last time, Myra,' I said, as we were coming out of the shop doorway, 'I've struck up with Eunice again.'

She didn't say anything for a minute. Then she said 'You won't be seeing her every night, will you? I could see you in between.'

'Out of the question!' I said, 'I warned you, didn't I? You can't say I ain't been fair. I told you from the start you was only a fill-in.'

'Here,' she said, tugging at the rolled lapels of my coat, 'make it next Thursday at the usual place, and if you don't come it'll be alright.'

'Okay,' I said quickly, for I didn't want them pulling out of shape. 'But I can promise you I'll not be there.'

'Come—if you feel like it,' she said.

That's got rid of you, mate, I thought to myself as I strolled home, and what a relief too! But when Thursday came round I was there waiting for her. Eunice was very good in her way, but it needed a bit of Myra to get her down. That started a caper of meeting Myra on my free nights, and some nights I'd meet her on my way back home. But come one Sunday and she must have had them on her proper:

'If I'm good enough to meet at half-past eleven,' she said, 'I'm good enough to meet at half-past seven; and if I'll do for a Thursday I don't see why I'm not up to scratch for a Saturday!'

'What you hinting at?' It griped me to hear her putting on airs.

'I'm not playing second-fiddle—'

'Second-fiddle! blimey, you said that well! You're bleedin' lucky to be in the band at all, you are! SECOND-FIDDLE—an' me only seeing you out of sympathy!'

I was going to give her a swipe, see, to lend weight to my words, when she ups with her mitts and grabs me by the collar and with one mad tug she ripped the lot apart. I all but collapsed on the spot, for just like some people can't stand the sight of blood I can't bear to hear anything tearing especially if it's mine. I put my fingers up to estimate the damage, and at only the first touch I knew it was beyond repair. 'If I could only lay my hands on you!' I shouted after her. All I got out of her was a long-drawn-out raspberry.

There comes one night a week later and I'm doing a bit of smooching with Eunice, when she says to me: 'What're you thinkin' about?'

'Who—me?' I says. 'What d'you mean, what am I thinking about?'

'You've got something on your mind,' she says. 'I can see by the look in your eyes.'

'Come off it,' I says.

'You know what,' she says. 'You've got that Myra on your mind.'

As soon as she said it I knew she was right.

'You know, Eunice,' I said, 'I think you're right.'

'I knew I was. Goodnight.'

And it's been the same ever since. I've met a dozen or more Eunices, and though I've respected every one I've never given them a second thought after packing in. But that blasted little Myra, drip that she is, is still on my mind. Understand me, I don't want her no more than fly-in-the-air, and I wouldn't please her so far as put my finger up—that would bring her running—yet the gorge fair chokes me when I think of other blokes going with her.

Advice to the Lovelorn

I

Miss Ann Austin came briskly into her little cupboard of a room at the back of the *Evening Planet* office. She hung up her hat and coat, opened her rolltop desk, put her small handbag carefully in a drawer, and looked at herself in a greenish mirror that hung secretly on a hook in the recess under the pigeonholes. She took the rubber hood off her typewriter, poured three paper cupfuls of drinking water on the potted geranium on the windowledge, wound up the cheap clock on top of the desk, and moved it forward ten minutes to compensate for what it had lost during the night. Now she was ready for work. As she wound up the clock, the usual thought occurred to her—when would she be able to buy herself the handsome little wrist watch she coveted? There were a lot of them in the jeweller's shop on Park Row, and she admired them every morning on her way to the office. But when one is supporting one's self and an invalid mother in an uptown apartment, and has to pay for a woman to come in during the day to lend a hand, all on fifty dollars a week, wrist watches have to wait. However, as Ann made the daily correction in her laggard clock she used to say to herself: 'There's a better time coming.' She was not devoid of humour, you see.

Then the office boy would bring in the big pile of morning mail, grinning as he laid it on the pull-out slide of her desk. He may be excused for grinning, because Ann was the kind of creature who would bring a smile to the surliest face. She was just a nice size, with a face that was both charming and sensible, and merry brown eyes (when it wasn't too close to the first of the month). Also, that pile of mail *was* rather amusing. Those letters, so many of them written on cheap pink or blue stationery and addressed in un-sophisticated handwriting, were not directed to Miss Ann Austin, but to 'Cynthia', and the office boy knew pretty well the kind of messages that were in them. For Ann, under the pseudonym of 'Cynthia', conducted the *Planet*'s department of Advice to the Lovelorn, and daily several score of puzzled or distracted beings bared their hearts to her. The pile of letters was growing bigger, too. The *Planet*, which was not a very flourishing paper just at that time, had started the Advice to the Lovelorn department a few months before, and had put Ann in charge of it because she had done so well writing sob stories. It was beginning to 'pull' quite surprisingly as a circulation feature, especially since her smiling little picture, vignetted in a cut with a border of tiny hearts, had been put at the head of the column. Under the cut was the legend: 'Cynthia, a Sympathetic Adviser in Matters of the Heart.' Ann didn't know whether to be pleased or not at the growing popularity of her feature. This was not quite the kind of thing she had hoped for when she entered the newspaper world. But—the more letters there were from the lovelorn, the sooner she might get that needed raise.

With a little sigh she got out her penknife, began slitting the envelopes, ceased to be Ann Austin and became Cynthia, the sage and gentle arbiter over her troubled parliament of love.

It was a task that required no small discretion and tact, because Cynthia, whatever her private misgivings, tried to perform it with some honest idealism. In the first place, the letters that were obviously merely humorous, or were amorous attempts to inveigle her into private correspondence, were discarded. Then the letters to be used in the next day's column had to be selected, and laid aside to be printed with her comment on the ethical or sociological problems involved. The remaining letters had all to be answered, and data noted down that would be useful in compiling the pamphlet '1001 Problems of Courtship' that the managing editor insisted on her preparing. He said it would be great circulation dope. Ann didn't care much for the managing editor, Mr Sikes. He had a way of coming into her room, closing the door behind him, leaning over her desk, and saying: 'Well, how's little Miss Cupid?' If it hadn't been for that habit of his, Ann would have spoken to him about a raise before now. But she had an uneasy feeling that it would not be pleasing to put herself in the position of asking him favours. She would have been still more disturbed if she had known that some of the boys in the city room used to talk about 'Cupid and Sikey' when they saw him visit her room. They said it angrily, because Ann was a general office favourite. Even the coloured elevator man had brought his wooing problems to her one day, wanting to be reassured as to his technique.

Mainly her letters exhibited the seamy side of Love's purple mantle. You see, when lovers are perfectly happy, they don't write to the papers about it. And when she pondered gravely over 'Broken-hearted's' letter saying that she has just learned that a perfectly splendid fellow she is so infatuated with has a wife and three children in Detroit; or over 'Puzzled's' inquiry as to whether she is 'a bum sport' because she wouldn't let the dark young man kiss her good-night, she sometimes said to herself that Napoleon was right. Napoleon, you remember, remarked that Love causes more unhappiness than anything else in the world. And then she would turn to her typewriter, and put under 'Puzzled's' inquiry:

> No, 'Puzzled,' do not let him kiss you unless you are betrothed. If any one is a 'bum sport' it is he for wanting to do so. If he 'always kisses the girls good-night when he has had a good time,' he is not your sort. A man that does not respect a girl before marriage will certainly not respect her afterward.

After she had typed these replies she always hastily took the paper out of her typewriter and tucked it away in her desk. She did not like the idea of Mr Sikes coming in and reading it over her shoulder, as he had done once. That was the time she had used the quotation 'Pains of Love are sweeter far than all other pleasures are' in answering 'Desolate'. The managing editor had repeated the verse in a way that both angered and alarmed her.

This particular morning, among the other letters was one that interested her both by the straightforward simplicity of its statement and by the clear, vigorous handwriting on sensible plain notepaper. It ran thus:

> Dear Cynthia,
> I am a young business man, very much in love, and I need your help. I have fallen in love with a girl who does not know me. I do not even know her name but I know her by sight, and I know where she works. She looks like the only one for me, but I don't want to do anything disrespectful. Would it be a mistake for me to call at her office and try to get a chance to meet her? Do you think she would be offended? She looks very adorable. Please tell me honestly what you think.
> Respectfully yours,
> Sincerity

Wearied by the maunderings of many idiotic flappers and baby vamps, this appeal attracted her. She put it into the column for the following day, writing underneath it:

> You never can tell, 'Sincerity'! It all depends upon you. If you are the right kind of man, she ought not to be offended. Why not take a chance? Faint heart never won fair lady.

It was trying enough, Ann used to think, to have to pore over the troubles of her lovelorn clients on paper; but the worst times were when they came to call on her at the office. Fortunately this did not happen very often, for the stricken maidens and young Lochinvars who make up the chief support of such columns as hers are safely and busily shut up among typewriters and filing cases during the daytime; their wounds do not begin to burn intolerably until about five-thirty p.m. But now and then some forlorn and baffled creature would find his or her way to 'Cynthia' and ask her advice. She would listen sympathetically, apply such homely febrifuge as her inexperienced but wise heart suggested to her, and after the patient had gone she would add the case to her list of 1001 Problems. The material for the pamphlet was growing rapidly.

One morning, while the managing editor was in her room asking her how soon the booklet would be ready, the office boy brought in a card neatly engraved *Mr Arthur Caldwell*. Now as a rule Cynthia did not see masculine visitors, because (after one or two trying experiences) she had found that they were inclined to transfer to her the heart that someone else had bruised. But in this case she welcomed the caller because Mr Sikes was being annoyingly facetious. He had looked over her laboriously gathered data for the 1001 Problems, and had said: 'Well, you're getting to be quite an experienced little girl in these matters, hey?' He had seemed disposed to linger on the topic with pleasure. Therefore Cynthia told the office boy to send Mr Caldwell in, though the name meant nothing to her. Mr Sikes went out, and the caller was introduced.

Mr Caldwell proved to be a young man, quite as nice-looking as the collar-advertising young men without being so desperately handsome. Cynthia liked him from the first glance. There was something that seemed very genuine about his soft collar and his candid, clean-shaven face and the little brown brief-case he carried. He had on brown woollen socks, too, she noticed, in one of those quick feminine observations. He seemed very embarrassed, and his face suddenly went ruby red.

'Is this Cynthia?' he said.

'Yes,' said Ann, pushing aside a mass of lovelorn correspondence, and wondering what the trouble could be.

'My name's Caldwell,' he said. 'Look here, I suppose you'll think me an awful idiot, but I wanted to ask your advice. I—I wrote you a letter the other day, and your answer in the column made me think that perhaps you wouldn't mind giving me some help. I wrote that letter signed "Sincerity".'

He was obviously ill at ease, and Ann tried to help him out.

'I remember the letter perfectly,' she said. 'Did you take my advice?'

'Well, I'm a bit uncertain about it,' he said. 'I just wanted to explain to you a little more fully, and see what you think. You see I happened to see this girl one day, going into her office. I suppose the idea about love at first sight is all exploded, but I had a hunch as soon as I saw her that—Oh, well, that I would like to know her. I've seen her going in and out of the building, but she has never seen me, never even heard of me. I don't know any one who can introduce me to her, and I can't just walk up to her and tell her I'm crazy about her. They don't do that except in Shakespeare. I don't know much about girls and I thought maybe you could suggest some way in which I could meet her without frightening her.'

Ann pondered. She liked the young man's way of putting his problem, and it was plain from his genuine embarrassment that he was sincere.

'I'd love to help you, if I could,' she said. 'It seems to me that the only way to go about it is to arrange some business with the firm she works for, and try to meet her that way. Couldn't that be done?'

'She's secretary to one of the big bugs in the Telephone Company,' he said. 'I'm in the publishing business. I don't see any way in which I could fake up a business connection there. The worst of it is, there may be a dozen fellows in love with her already, for all I know. I suppose I might get a job with the Telephone Company, but by the time I had worked up far enough to have an excuse for going into the vice-president's office where she works, someone else might have married her.' He laughed, a boyish, ingratiating chuckle.

'It does seem pretty hard,' said Ann. 'I don't know what to say.' She had a mental picture of the unknown fair one, going in and out of the big Telephone Company's building on Dey Street, unaware of the admiring glances of this bashful admirer. 'I'll bet the men she knows aren't half as nice as he is,' she said to herself.

'I happen to know that she reads your column,' said Caldwell. 'I suppose there isn't any way I could get in touch with her through that?'

'If there's any legitimate way I can help,' Ann said, 'I'll be glad
to. But I hardly see what I can do.'

'Well, thanks awfully,' he said. 'If I get a chance to meet her,
will you let me come in again and tell you about it? Perhaps you
would let me mention your name as a reference, in regard to my
respectability I mean?'

'Surely you can give her better references than that? You see,
I don't know so very much about you, Mr Caldwell.'

'In matters like this,' he said, 'I guess you're the Big Authority.
And by the way, do you ever do any book reviewing? I work for
Fawcett and Company, the publishers, and we'd like immensely
to have your comment on some of our love stories. Can I send you
some books?'

'I can't promise to review them,' said Ann, rather pleased,
because this seemed to her a way to earn a little extra money. 'But
I'll speak to the literary editor, and we'll see.'

'Suppose I send them to your home address,' said Caldwell. 'I
know what a newspaper office is, if I send them here someone else
might snitch them. Give me your street number, and you'll be
spared the trouble of taking them home to read.'

'That's very kind of you,' said Ann. 'Miss Ann Austin, 527 West
150th Street. Well, you let me know what happens about your fair
lady. I wish you all sorts of luck!'

When Arthur Caldwell got outside the office, he looked down
Park Row to where the great Telephone Building rose up behind
the brown silhouette of St Paul's.

'Caldwell,' he said to himself, 'you're an infernal liar! But it
pays! I'll figure out some way. While there's life there's hope.'

He set out for the subway, but paused again to meditate.

'Ann Austin!' he said. 'By George, she's a queen.'

II

It is not the purpose of this tale to tell in detail how Arthur Caldwell
laid siege to Ann Austin. He was a cautious man, and for some
time he contented himself by presenting occasional reports of his
progress with the damsel of the Telephone Company. Ann, in her
friendly and unselfish way, was delighted to hear, a few days later,
that he had met his ideal. Then, averring that he needed further
counsel, Arthur persuaded her to have lunch with him one day;
and Ann, convinced that the young man was in love with someone

else, saw no reason why this should not be done. Perhaps it was a little odd that at their various meetings they should have talked so much of themselves, their ambitions, the books they had been reading, and so on; and so little of the Telephone lady. But surely it was strictly a matter of business that Arthur should send Miss Austin some of Fawcett's novels, for her to review in the *Planet*; and equally a professional matter that he should discuss with her her opinion of them. And then came the day when Arthur called up to say that things were going so well with the Telephone lady that he wanted Cynthia to meet her; and would she join them in St Paul's Churchyard at half-past twelve? Ann, with just a curious little unanalysed twinge in her heart, agreed to do so.

But when she reached the bench in the graveyard, where a bright autumn sunshine filled the clearing among those tremendous buildings, Arthur was there alone.

'Where's Alice?' said Ann, innocently—for such was the name Arthur had always given the lady of the Telephone Company.

'She couldn't come,' he said. 'But I want to show you her picture.'

They sat down on the bench, and he took out of his pocket a copy of the noon edition of the *Planet*. He turned to the feature page, and displayed the little cut of Cynthia at the head of the Lovelorn column.

'There,' he said, stoutly (though his heart was tremulous within him), 'there, you adorable little thing, there she is.'

It would be pleasant to linger over this scene, but, as I have just said, this is not our *dénouement*, but only an incident. Ann, shot through with delicious pangs of doubt and glory and anger, asked for explanations.

'And do you mean to say there never was any Alice, the beautiful Telephone blonde?' she said. 'What a fraud you are!'

'Of course not,' he said. 'You dear, delightful innocent, I just had to cook up some excuse for coming up to see you. And you can't be angry with me now, Ann, because in your own answer to Sincerity's letter you said the girl ought not to be offended. You told me to take a chance! Just think what self-control I had, that first time I came up to see you, not to blurt out the truth.'

And then he tore off a scrap of margin from the newspaper and measured her finger for a ring.

III

There were happy evenings that winter, when Ann, after finishing her stint at the office, would hasten up their rendezvous at Piazza's little Italian table d'hôte. Here, over the minestrone soup and the spaghetti and that strong Italian coffee that seems to have a greenish light round the edges of the liquid (and an equally greenish taste), they would discuss their plans and platitudes, just as lovers always have and always will. As for Ann, the light of a mystical benevolence shone in her as she conned her daily pile of broken hearts in the morning mail. More than ever she felt that she, who had seen the true flame upon the high altar, had a duty to all perplexed and random followers of the gleam who had gone astray in their search. Aware more keenly that the troubled appeals of 'Tearful' and 'Little Pal', however absurd, were the pains of genuine heartache, she became more and more tender in her comments, and her correspondence grew apace. Now that she knew that her job need not go on forever she tried honestly to run the column with all her might. How stern she was with the flirt and the vamp and the jilt; how sympathetic with the wounded on Love's great battle-field. 'Great stuff, great stuff!' Mr Sikes would cry, in his coarse way, and complimented her on the increasing 'kick' of her department. Knowing that he attributed the accelerated pulse of the Lovelorn column to mere cynicism on her part, she did not dare wear her ring in the office for fear of being joked about it. She used to think sadly that because she had made sympathy with lovers a matter of trade, she herself, now she was in love, could hope for no understanding. Although she hardly admitted it, she longed for the day when she could drop the whole thing.

One evening Arthur met her at Piazza's, radiant. He was going off on a long business trip for his publishing house, and they had promised him a substantial raise when he returned. They sat down to dinner together in the highest spirits. Arthur, in particular, was in a triumphant mood: the publishing world, it seemed, lay under his feet.

'Great news, hey?' he said. 'We'll be able to get married in the spring, and you can kick out of that miserable job.'

'But, Arthur,' she said, 'you know I have to take care of Mother. Don't you think it would be wiser if I went on with the work for a while, until your next raise comes? It would help a good deal, and we'd be able to put a little away for a rainy day.'

'What?' he said. 'Do you think I'm going to have my wife doing that lovelorn stuff in the paper every day? It'd make me a laughing stock if it ever got out. No, *sir*! I haven't said much about it, because I knew it couldn't be helped; but believe me, honey, that isn't the right kind of job for you. I've often wondered you didn't feel that yourself.'

Ann was a little nettled that he should put it that way. Whatever her private distaste for the Lovelorn column, it had served her well in a difficult time, and had paid the doctor's bills at home. And she knew how much honest devotion she had put into the task of trying to give helpful counsel.

'At any rate,' she said, 'it was through the column that we first met.'

What evil divinity sat upon Arthur's tongue that he could not see this was the moment for a word of tenderness? But a young man flushed with his first vision of business success, the feeling that now nothing can prevent him from 'making good', is likely to be obtuse to the finer shades of intercourse.

'Of course, dear, I could see you were different from the usual sob sister of the press,' he said. 'I could see you didn't really fall for that stuff. It's because I love you so, I want to get you out of that cheap, degrading sensational work. Most of those letters you get are only fakes, anyway. I think Love ought to be sacred, not used as mere circulation bait for a newspaper.'

Ann was a high-spirited girl, and this blunt criticism touched her in that vivid, quivering region of the mind where no woman stops to reason. But she made an honest attempt to be patient.

'But, Arthur,' she said; 'there's nothing really cheap and degraded in trying to help others who haven't had the same advantages we have. I know a lot of the letters I print are silly and absurd, but not more so than some of the books you publish.'

'Now, listen,' he said, loftily, 'we won't quarrel about this. I don't want you to go on with the job, that's all. It isn't fair to you. You may take the work seriously, and put all sorts of idealism into it, but it's not the right kind of job for a refined girl. How about the men in the office? I'll bet I know what *they* think of it. They probably think it's a devil of a good joke, and laugh about it among themselves. Don't you think I've seen that managing editor leering at you? That sort of thing cheapens a girl among decent men. Every Lovelace in town feels he has a right to send you mash-notes, I guess.'

Ann was furious.

'Well, you're the only one I ever paid any attention to,' she said, blazing at him. 'I'm sorry you think I've cheapened myself. I guess I have, by letting you interfere with my affairs.'

She slipped the ring from her finger, and thrust it at him. Arthur saw, too late, what he had done. She listened in scornful silence to his miserable attempts to console her, which were doubly handicapped by the old waiter hovering near. She was still adamant while he took her up town. The only thing she said was when she reached the door of her apartment.

'I don't want you to cheapen yourself. You needn't come any more.'

By this time Arthur also was thoroughly angry. The next morning he went away on his business trip, realizing for the first time that he who has the pass key to a human heart treads among dangerous explosives.

IV

How different the little room in the *Planet* office looked to Ann when she returned, with a sick heart, to her work the next morning. Everything was just the same—the geranium on its windowledge, that seemed to survive both the eddying hot air from the steampipes beneath it and the daily douche of iced drinking water; the noisily ticking inaccurate little clock; the dusty typewriter. All were the same, and there was the pile of morning letters from Love's battered henchmen. To office boy and casual reporter Ann herself seemed the usual cheerful charmer with her crisp little white collar and dark, alluring hair. Her swift, capable hands sped over the pile of letters, slitting the envelopes and sorting the outcries into some classification of her own. Outwardly nothing had altered, but everything seemed to have lost its meaning. What a desolate emptiness gaped beneath the firm routine of her daily life. She was struck by the irony of the fact that the only one in the office who seemed to notice that something was amiss was the one person whom she disliked—Mr Sikes. He came in about something or other, and then stayed, looking at her intently.

'You look sick,' he said. 'What's the matter, is the love feast getting on your nerves?'

With a queer twitching at the corners of her mouth, she forced herself to say some trifling remark. He leaned over her and put his hand on hers. She caught the strong cigarry whiff of his clothes, which sickened her.

'Too much love in the abstract,' he said, insinuatingly. 'What you need is a little love in the concrete.'

If he—or any one—had spoken tenderly to her, she would have burst into tears. But the boorishness of his words was just the tonic she needed. She looked at him with flashing eyes, and was about to say: 'Keep to some topic you understand.' Then she dared not say it, for now she could not run the risk of losing her job. She faced him steadily, in angry silence. He left the room, and the little green-tarnished mirror under the pigeonholes saw tears for the first time.

The irony of her position moved her cruelly when she began her task of dealing with the correspondants. Here she was, giving helpful, cheery advice, posing as all-wise in these matters, when her own love affair had come so miserably to grief. In the ill-written scrawls on scented and scalloped paper she could hear an echo of her own suffering. 'Hopeless' and 'Uncertain' and 'Miss Eighteen' got very tender replies that day. And how she laid the lash upon 'Beau Brummel' and 'Disillusioned', those self-assured young men, who had chosen that mail to contribute their views on the flirtatious and unreliable qualities of modern girls.

The bitterness of her paradoxical task became dulled as the days went on, but there were other troubles, too, to bother her. Her mother, quick and querulous to detect unhappiness, fell into one of her nervous spells, and the doctor had to be called in again. The woman-by-the-day got blood-poisoning in her arm, and could not come. The landlord gave notice of a coming raise in rent. A fat letter came from Arthur, and in a flush of passion she destroyed it unread. If it hadn't been such a fat letter, she said to herself, it wouldn't have annoyed her so to see it. But she wasn't going to wade through pages of explanation of just what he had meant. She was still cut to the quick when she remembered the cavalier and easy way in which he had scoffed at her work. And then, as time went by, she found herself moving into a new mood—no longer one of exaggerated tenderness toward her clients, but a feeling almost cynical. 'They're all fools, just as I am,' she said.

One morning she found on her desk a note from the managing editor:

Dear Miss Cupid,

We've made some changes in our budget, and I've been authorized to fatten your envelope $15 a week. I'm glad to do this, because the Lovelorn stuff is going big. Just keep kidding them along and everything will be fine. Maybe some day we can syndicate it. Hope this will cheer you up, don't look so blue at your friends.

Sikes

There had been a time when the tone and phrasing of this note might have seemed offensive, but in the numbness of despondency Ann had felt lately it was a fine burst of rosy warmth. Thank God, she said to herself, something has broken my way at last! She wondered if she had been mistaken in Sikes, after all? Perhaps he was really a friend of hers, and she had misunderstood his odd ways.

That day at noon she went down to the cashier's department to cash a small cheque. There was no one in the cage, but in the adjoining compartment, behind a wall of filing cases, she could hear two girls talking. One of them said:

'I see Sikes has put through a raise for Lovelorn. Pretty soft for her, hey?'

'She'll have to give value received, I guess,' said the other. 'Sikes figures if he puts that over for her, she'll fall for him. She's been stalling him for quite a while, but I suppose he's got her fixed now.'

She fled, aghast, ran down to another floor so as not to be seen, and took the elevator. Out on the street she walked mechanically along Park Row and found herself opposite St Paul's. She wandered in and sat down on a bench. It was a chilly day, and the churchyard was nearly empty.

So this was Sikes's friendliness; and she, utterly innocent even in thought, was already the subject of vulgar office gossip. For the first time there broke in upon her, with bitter force, the knowledge that no matter how easy it may be to counsel others, few of us are wise in our own affairs. Pitiable paradox: she, the 'sympathetic adviser in matters of the heart', had made shipwreck of her own happiness. How right Arthur had been, and how childish and mad she, to reject his just instinct. It was true: she had made use of Love for mere newspaper circulation; and now Love had died between her hands. Well, this was the end. No matter what happened, she could not go on with the job. Cold and trembling with nervousness, she returned to her desk, to finish her column for the next day.

On her typewriter lay some letters, which had come in while she was out. She opened one, and read.

Dear Cynthia,

I am in great trouble, please help me. I am in love with a fellow and know he is all right and we would be very happy together. We were engaged to be married, and everything was lovely. But he objected to the work I was doing, said it was not a good job for a girl and that I ought to give it up. I knew he was right, but the way he said it made me mad. I guess I am hot-tempered and stubborn—anyway, I told him to mind his own business, and he went away. Now I am heart-broken, because I love him and I know he loves me. Tell me what to do.

                                                                Jessie

Ann sat looking at the cheap blue paper with the initial J gaudily embossed upon it in gilt. In the sprawling lines of unlettered handwriting she saw an exact parallel to her own unhappy rupture with Arthur. How much more clearly we can see the answer in others' tangles than in our own! Jessie, with her pathetic pretentious gilt initial, knew that she had been in the wrong, and was brave enough to want to make amends. And she—had she not been less true to Love than Jessie? Her false pride and obstinacy had brought their own punishment. Seeing the situation through Jessie's eyes, she could read her duty plain. Arthur, no doubt, was through with her forever, but she must play the game no less.

She put Jessie's letter at the head of the Lovelorn column for the next day. Under it she wrote:

Certainly, dear Jessie, if you feel you were in the wrong, you ought to take the first step toward making up. Probably he was tactless in criticizing you, but I am sure he only did it because he had your true interest at heart. So write him a nice letter and be happy together. Your friend Cynthia hopes it will all come out all right, because she has seen other cases like this where false pride caused great suffering. If he is the right man, he will love you all the more after he gets your letter.

Ann sent up her copy to the composing room, and then going to a telephone booth she called up Fawcett and Company and asked for Mr Caldwell.

'Mr Caldwell's not here any longer,' said the girl.

'Serves me right,' said Ann to herself. 'Can you tell me where I can find him?' she asked, wondering how it was that one so miserable could still speak in such a pleasant and apparently unconcerned tone of voice.

The Fawcett operator switched her to another wire.

'I'm sorry,' said a stenographer, 'Mr Caldwell left here about

two weeks ago. He's got a job out of town—in Boston, I think.
I can find out for you in the morning if you'll call again.'

'Never mind,' said Ann.

She had a horror of facing Mr Sikes in her present wretchedness,
so before she went home she wrote him a note, resigning her job,
and asking permission to leave as soon as possible.

The next day she had to nerve herself to face his protests, and
the friendly remarks of all the staff when the news spread. It was
a hideous ordeal, but she managed to get through it smiling. But
by evening she was inwardly a wreck. In her present mood, she
had an instinctive longing to revisit the shabby little restaurant
where she and Arthur had spent so many happy hours. She knew
it would give her pain; but she felt that pain was what she needed—
sharp, clean, insistent pain to ease the oppression and disgust of
what she had been through. Remorse, she felt, is surgical in action:
it cuts away foul tissues of the mind. She could not, without pre-
paratory discipline, face her mother's outcry at hearing she had
given up her job.

V

In the crisp blue evening air the bright front of Piazza's café shone
with a warm and generous lustre. From sheer force of habit, her
heart lightened a little as she climbed the stairs and entered the
familiar place, where festoons of red and green paper decoration
criss-crossed above the warm, soup-flavoured, tobacco-fogged
room. There was a clatter of thick dishes and a clamour of
talk.

'One?' said the head waiter, his wiry black hair standing erect
as though in surprise.

She nodded, and followed him down the narrow aisle. There
was the little table, in the corner under the stair, where they had
always sat. A man was there, reading a newspaper.... Her heart
felt very strange, as though it had dropped a long way below its
usual place. It was Arthur, and he was smiling at her as though
nothing had happened. He was getting up ... he was shaking hands
with her ... how natural it all seemed!

Like all really great crises, it was over in a flash. She found herself
sitting at the little table, taking off her gloves in the most casual
fashion. Arthur was whispering outrageous things. How fine it is
that everybody talks so loud in Italian table d'hôtes, and the waiters
crash the dishes round so recklessly!

Arthur's talk seemed to be in two different keys, partly for the benefit of old Tonio, the waiter, and partly for her alone.

'Well, here you are! I wondered how soon you'd get here ... *Have you forgiven me, dearest?* ... Do you want some minestrone? ... *Why didn't you answer my letters, brownest eyes?* ... Yes, and some of the near-beer. ... *Darling, it was all my fault. I wrote to tell you so. Didn't you get my letter?*'

After all, at such times there isn't much explaining done. A happy reconciliation is the magic of a moment, and no explanations are necessary. The trouble just drops away, and life begins again from the last kind thing that was said. All Ann could do was whisper:

'No, Arthur—it was I who was wrong. I—I've given up the Lovelorn.'

And then, after a sudden moisture of eye on both sides, the steaming minestrone came on in its battered leaden tureen from which the silver plating disappeared long ago, and under pretence of serving her soup Arthur stretched out his hand. She put out hers to meet it, and found the ring slipped deftly back on her finger.

'But, Arthur,' she said, presently, 'I thought you were out of town.'

'I was,' he said. 'I've got a new job, with King and Company in Boston. A good job, too, we can be married right away, and you don't need to worry.'

'Well, how did you happen to come here tonight? You didn't know I was going to be here, I didn't know it myself until an hour or so ago.'

'Perhaps I willed you to come, who knows?' he said, gaily. 'Have you been advising lovers all this while, and didn't know that they always haunt the scenes of former felicity? I've been in town several days, and came here every night.'

He produced a copy of the *Evening Planet* which he had been reading when she came in.

'I had a special reason for thinking you might come here to-night,' he said. 'This afternoon I read your column, and I saw Jessie's letter and your answer. What you said made me think that perhaps you might be willing to forgive me.'

Ann, once more safely enthroned on shining glory of her happi-, ness, felt that she could afford to tease him just a little.

'Ah,' she said, 'so you admit that some of those letters people write me *are* genuine, and that the answers do some good?'

He smiled at her and laid his hand over the ring, which out-glittered even the most newly nickelled of Piazza's cutlery.

'Yes, honey,' he said. 'I admit it. And I knew that Jessie's letter was genuine, because I wrote it myself.'

Stan Barstow

The Fury

There were times when Mrs Fletcher was sure her husband thought more of his rabbits than anything else in the world: more than tobacco and comfort, more than her—or the other woman. And this was one of those times, this Saturday morning as she looked out from the kitchen where she was preparing the dinner to where she could see Fletcher working absorbedly, and grooming his two favourite Angoras for the afternoon's show in Cressley.

She was a passionate woman who clung singlemindedly to what was hers, and was prepared to defend her rights with vigour. While courting Fletcher she had drawn blood on an erstwhile rival who had threatened to reassert her claims. Since then she had had worse things to contend with. Always, it seemed to her, there was something between her and her rightful possession of Fletcher. At the moment it was the rabbits. The big shed had been full of hutches at one time, but now Fletcher concentrated his attention on a handful of animals in which he had a steady faith. But there were still too many for Mrs Fletcher, who resented sharing him with anything or anybody, and the sight of his absorption now stirred feelings which brought unnecessary force to bear on the sharp knife with which she sliced potatoes for the pan.

'Got a special class for Angoras today,' Fletcher said later at the table. He was in a hurry to be off and he shovelled loaded spoons of jam sponge pudding into his mouth between the short sentences. 'Might do summat for a change. Time I had a bit o' luck.' He was washed and clean now, his square, ruddily handsome face close shaven, the railway porter's uniform discarded for his best grey worsted. The carrying-case with the rabbits in it stood by the door.

Mrs Fletcher gave no sign of interest. She said 'D'you think you'll be back in time for t'pictures?'

Fletcher gulped water. He had a way of drinking which showed his fine teeth. 'Should be,' he answered between swallows. 'Anyway, if you're so keen to go why don't you fix up with Mrs Sykes?'

'I should be able to go out with you, Saturday nights,' Mrs

Fletcher said. 'Mrs Sykes has a husband of her own to keep her company.'

'Fat lot o' company he is Saturday night,' Fletcher said dryly. 'Or Sunday for that matter . . . Anyway I'll try me best. Can't say fairer than that, can I?'

'Not as long as you get back in time.'

Fletcher pushed back his chair and stood up. 'I don't see why not. It shouldn't be a long job today. It isn't a big show. I should be back by half-past seven at latest.'

'Well, just see 'at you are,' she said.

She stood by the window and watched him go down the road in the pale sunshine, carrying case, slung from one shoulder, prevented from jogging by a careful hand. He cut a handsome, well-set-up figure when he was dressed up, she thought. Often too handsome, too well-set-up for her peace of mind.

By half-past seven she was washed, dressed, and lightly made-up ready for the evening out. But Fletcher had not returned. And when the clock on the mantelshelf chimed eight there was still no sign of him. It was after ten when he came. She was sitting by the fire, the wireless blaring unheard, her knitting needles flashing with silent fury.

'What time d'you call this?' she said, giving him no chance to speak. 'Saturday night an' me sittin' here like a doo-lal while you gallivant up an' down as you please.'

He was obviously uneasy, expecting trouble. 'I'm sorry,' he said. 'I meant to get back. I thought I should, but there were more than I expected. It took a long time. . . .' He avoided her eyes as he went into the passage to hang up his overcoat. 'Didn't win owt, either,' he muttered, half to himself. 'Not a blinkin' sausage.'

'You knew I specially wanted to see that picture, didn't you?' Mrs Fletcher said, her voice rising. 'I've been telling you all week, but that makes no difference, does it! What does your·wife matter once you get off with your blasted rabbits, eh?'

As though he had not heard her Fletcher opened the case and lifted out one of the rabbits and held it to him, stroking the long soft fur. 'You just wasn't good enough, was you, eh?' The rabbit blinked its pink eyes in the bright electric light. 'Nivver mind: you're a beauty all t' same.'

His ignoring of her maddened Mrs Fletcher almost more than she could bear. 'I'm talking to you!' she stormed.

'I heard you; an' I said I'm sorry. What more do you want?'

'Oh, you're sorry, and that's the end of it, I suppose. That's all my Saturday night's worth, is it?'

'I couldn't help it,' Fletcher said. 'I said I couldn't help it.' He put the rabbit back in the case and sat down to unlace his shoes. She watched him, eyes glittering, mouth a thin trap of temper.

'Aye, you said so. You said you'd be home at half-past seven an' all, and we've seen what that was worth. How do I know what you've been up to while I've been sitting here by myself?'

He looked quickly up at her, his usual full colour deepening and spreading. 'What're you gettin' at now?'

'You know what I'm gettin' at.' Her head nodded grimly.

Fletcher threw down his shoes. 'I told you,' he said with throaty anger, 'an' that's all over. It's been finished with a long time. Why can't you let it rest, 'stead o' keep harping on about it?'

He stood up, and taking the carrying case, walked out in his slippers to the shed, leaving her to talk to the empty room. He always got away from her like that. She grabbed the poker and stabbed savagely at the fire.

On Sunday morning she was shaking a mat in the yard when her neighbour spoke to her over the fence.

'Did you get to the Palace this week, then, Mrs Fletcher?' Mrs Sykes asked her. 'Oh, but you did miss a treat. All about the early Christians and the cloak 'at Jesus wore on the cross. Lovely, it was, and ever so sad.'

'I wanted to see it,' Mrs Fletcher said, 'but Jim didn't get back from Cressley till late. His rabbits y'know.' She felt a strong desire to abuse him in her talk, but pride held her tongue. It was bad enough his being as he was without the shame of everyone's knowing it.

'Oh, aye, they had a show, didn't they?' Mrs Sykes said. 'Aye, I saw him in the bus station afterwards. He was talking to a woman I took to be your sister.'

Mrs Fletcher shot the other woman a look. What was she up to? She knew very well that her sister had lived down south these last twelve months. Her cheeks flamed suddenly and she turned her back on her neighbour and went into the house.

Fletcher was lounging, unshaven and in shirt sleeves, his feet propped up on the fireplace, reading the Sunday papers. She went for him as soon as she had put the thickness of the door between them and Mrs Sykes, who still lingered in the yard.

'You must think I'm stupid!'

'Eh?' Fletcher said, looking up. 'What's up now?'

'What's up? What's up? How can you find the face to sit there with your feet up and ask me that? You must think I'm daft altogether; but it's you 'at's daft, if you did but know it. Did you think you could get away with it? Did you really think so? You might ha' known somebody 'ud see you. And you had to do it in the bus station at that—a public place!'

'I don't even know what you're talking about,' Fletcher said, but his eyes gave him away.

'You'll brazen it out to the very end, won't you?' she said. 'You liar you. "Oh, I've made a mistake," he says. "I'll never see her again," he says. And what do you do but go running back to her the minute you think you can get away with it!'

Fletcher got up, throwing the newspaper to one side. 'I tell you I don't—' Then he stopped, the bluster draining out of him. 'All right,' he said quietly. 'If you'll calm down a minute I'll tell you.'

'You'll tell *me*!' Mrs Fletcher said. 'You'll tell me nothing any more. It's all lies, lies, lies every time you open your mouth. Well I've finished. Bad enough your rabbits, but I draw the line at fancy women. You promised me faithful you wouldn't see her again. You said it sitting in that very chair. And what was it worth, eh? Not a row o' buttons. What d'you think I feel like when me own neighbours tell me they've seen you carryin' on?'

'If you wouldn't listen so much to what t'neighbours say an' take notice o' what I have to tell you—' Fletcher began.

'I've done listening to you,' she said. 'Now I'm having my say.'

'Well, you'll say it to yourself, and rest o' t'street mebbe, but not to me.' He strode across the room and dragged down his coat. 'I'll go somewhere where I can talk to somebody 'at's not next door to a ravin' lunatic.'

'And stop there when you get there,' she told him. 'Go to her. Tell her I've had enough of you. See if she'll sit at home while you traipse about country-side with a boxful o' mucky vermin.'

He was at the door, pulling on his coat.

'And take your things,' she said. 'Might as well make a clean sweep while you're about it.'

'I'm going to our Tom's,' he said. 'I'll send for 'em tomorrow.'

'I'll have 'em ready,' she said.

When the door had closed behind him she stood for a moment, eyes glittering, nostrils dilated, her entire body stiff and quivering with rage. Then suddenly she plucked a vase from the mantelshelf and dashed it to pieces in the hearth. She clenched and unclenched her hands at her sides, her eyes seeking wildly as the fury roared impotently in her.

At half-past ten she was in the kitchen making her supper when she heard the front door open. She went through into the passage and her hands tightened involuntarily about the milk bottle she was holding as she saw Fletcher there.

'Well,' she said. 'Have you come for your things?' Her voice was tight and unnatural and Fletcher took it as a sign of her lingering anger.

He closed the door and stood sheepishly behind it, his eyes avoiding hers. 'I just thought I'd come an' see if you'd calmed down,' he said.

'I thought we'd heard the last of that this morning?' Her eyes were fixed, bright and unmoving, on his face, and Fletcher caught them with his own for an instant and looked away again.

'We were both a bit worked up like,' he said. 'I know how it is when you get mad. You do an' say a lot o' things you don't really mean. That you regret after.'

There was silence for a second before she said, the same tight, strained note in her voice, 'What things?'

'I mean like me walkin' out,' Fletcher said. 'All it needed was a bit o' quiet talkin' an' it wouldn't ha' come to that. It'd ha' been all right if only you'd listened to me.'

'I never expected you to come back,' she said, and moved almost trance-like, across the room to the fire, still watching him intently almost disbelievingly, as though she had expected that with his slamming of the door this morning he would walk off the edge of the world, never to be seen again.

He came over to the hearth to stand beside her. He started to put his hand on her shoulder, but as she moved away slightly he dropped his arm again and looked past her into the fire.

'What I said before, I meant,' he said, speaking quietly, earnestly, with the awkwardness of a man not used to expressing the finer feelings. 'I could ha' told you last night, only I didn't see any point. It was all forgotten as far as I was concerned. Finished. But she was waiting for me when I came out o' show. I told her I didn't want to see her again. There was never owt much between us anyway. But I couldn't get rid of her. She hung on like mad. An' when I looked at her, all painted an' powdered up, I found meself thinkin' what a great fool I'd been ever to risk losing all that mattered for a brazen baggage like her. It took me a couple of hours to get rid of her. She got proper nasty towards the end. Started shoutin' and swearin', right in the street. It was awful.' Fletcher sighed and shook his head and a shudder seemed to run through Mrs Fletcher. 'And I had to jump on a bus in the end and just leave her standing there. There was nowt else I could do bar give her a clout or summat....'

As he finished talking something seemed to snap inside Mrs Fletcher and she began to cry softly. He put his arm round her shoulders, tentatively at first, then, when she offered no resistance, with pressure, drawing her to him.

'Now, lass. Now, then. Cryin' won't do any good. We've had our little bust-up, an' now it's all over an' done with.'

'Oh, why didn't I listen?' she sobbed. 'None of this would have happened then.'

He drew her down into an armchair and held her to him. 'Never mind now, lass. No harm done. Don't cry any more.'

After a time, he said, 'I'll just nip out an' see to the rabbits, then we can get off up to bed.'

She held him to her. 'No leave 'em. Come to bed now.'

He smiled quietly, indulgently. 'Still a bit jealous, eh? Well I reckon they'll manage till morning.'

Later still, in the dark secret warmth of the bed, she clung to him again. 'Did you mean it?' she said. 'When you said you loved nobody but me?'

'I did,' he said.

'Say it, then,' she said, holding him hard.

'I love you, lass,' he said. 'Nobody but you. It'll be better in future. You'll see.'

She could have cried out then. Better in future! Oh, why hadn't she listened? Why, why, why? If only she had listened and heard him in time! For this moment was all she had. There could be no future: nothing past the morning when he would go out and find the rabbits slaughtered in their hutches.

Anthony Trollope

Malachi's Cove

On the northern coast of Cornwall, between Tintagel and Bos-
siney, down on the very margin of the sea, there lived not long
since an old man who got his living by saving seaweed from the
waves, and selling it for manure. The cliffs there are bold and fine,
and the sea beats in upon them from the north with a grand
violence; the margin of sand at high water is very narrow,—so
narrow that at spring-tides there is barely a footing there.

   Close upon this margin was the cottage or hovel of Malachi
Trenglos, the old man of whom I have spoken. But Malachi, or
old Glos, as he was commonly called by the people around him,
had not built his house absolutely upon the sand. There was a
fissure in the rock so great that at the top it formed a narrow ravine,
and so complete from the summit to the base that it afforded an
opening for a steep and rugged track from the top of the rock to
the bottom. This fissure was so wide at the bottom that it had
afforded space for Trenglos to fix his habitation on a foundation
of rock, and here he had lived for many years. In the early days
of his trade he had always carried the weed in a basket on his back
to the top, but latterly he had been possessed of a donkey which
had been trained to go up and down the steep track with a single
pannier over his loins, for the rocks would not admit of panniers
hanging by his side; and for this assistant he had built a shed
adjoining his own, and almost as large as that in which he himself
resided.

   But, as years went on, old Glos procured other assistance than
that of the donkey, and, indeed, had it not been so, the old man
must have given up his cabin and his independence and gone into
the workhouse at Camelford. For rheumatism had afflicted him,
old age had bowed him till he was nearly double, and by degrees
he became unable to attend the donkey on its upward passage to
the world above, or even to assist in rescuing the weed from the
waves.

   At the time to which our story refers Trenglos had not been up
the cliff for twelve months, and for the last six months he had done

nothing towards the furtherance of his trade. The real work of the business was done altogether by Mahala Trenglos, his granddaughter.

Mally Trenglos was known to all the farmers round the coast, and to all the small tradespeople in Camelford. She was a wild-looking, almost unearthly creature, with wild-flowing, black, uncombed hair, small in stature, with small hands and bright black eyes; but people said that she was very strong, and the children around declared that she worked day and night, and knew nothing of fatigue. As to her age there were many doubts. Some said she was ten, and others five-and-twenty, but the reader may be allowed to know that at this time she had passed her twentieth birthday. The old people spoke well of Mally, because she was so good to her grandfather; and it was said of her that though she carried to him a little gin and tobacco almost daily, she bought nothing for herself. But she had no friends, and but few acquaintances among people of her own age. They said that she was fierce and ill-natured, that she had not a good word for any one, and that she was, complete at all points, a thorough little vixen. The young men did not care for her; for, as regarded dress, all days were alike with her. She never made herself smart on Sundays. She was generally without stockings, and seemed to care not at all to exercise any feminine attractions. All days were the same to her in regard to dress; and, indeed, till lately, all days had been the same to her in other respects. Old Malachi had never been seen inside a place of worship since he had taken to live under the cliff.

But within the last two years Mally had submitted herself to the teaching of the clergyman at Tintagel, and had appeared at church on Sundays. But she made no difference in her dress on these occasions. She took her place on a low stone seat just inside the church door, clothed as usual in her thick red serge petticoat and loose brown serge jacket, such being the apparel which she had found to be best adapted for her hard and perilous work among the waters. She had pleaded to the clergyman when he attacked her on the subject of church attendance that she had got no church-going clothes. He had explained to her that she would be received there without distinction to her clothing. Mally had taken him at his word, and had gone, with a courage which certainly deserved admiration, though I doubt whether there was not mingled with it an obstinacy which was less admirable.

For people said that old Glos was rich, and that Mally might have proper clothes if she chose to buy them. Mr Polwarth, the clergyman, who, as the old man could not come to him, went down the rocks to the old man, did make some hint on the matter in Mally's absence. But old Glos, who had been patient with him on other matters, turned upon him so angrily when he made an allusion to money, that Mr Polwarth found himself obliged to give that matter up, and Mally continued to sit upon the stone bench in her short serge petticoat, with her long hair streaming down her face. She did so far sacrifice to decency as on such occasions to tie up her back hair with an old shoe-string.

As to Mally's indefatigable industry there could be no manner of doubt, for the quantity of seaweed which she and the donkey amassed between them was very surprising. Old Glos, it was declared, had never collected half what Mally gathered together; but then the article was becoming cheaper, and it was necessary that the exertion should be greater. So Mally and the donkey toiled and toiled, and the seaweed came up in heaps which surprised those who looked at her little hands and light form. Was there not some one who helped her at nights, some fairy, or demon, or the like? Mally was so snappish in her answers to people that she had no right to be surprised if ill-natured things were said of her.

No one ever heard Mally Trenglos complain of her work, but about this time she was heard to make great and loud complaints of the treatment she received from some of her neighbours. It was known that she went with her plaints to Mr Polwarth; and when he could not help her, or did not give her such instant help as she needed, she went to the office of a certain attorney at Camelford, who was not likely to prove himself a better friend than Mr Polwarth.

Now the nature of her injury was as follows. The place in which she collected her seaweed was a little cove; the people had come to call it Malachi's Cove from the name of the old man who lived there;—which was so formed, that the margin of the sea therein could only be reached by the passage from the top down to Trenglos's hut. The breadth of the cove when the sea was out might perhaps be two hundred yards, and on each side the rocks ran out in such a way that both from north and south the domain of Trenglos was guarded from intruders. And this locality had been well chosen for its intended purpose.

There was a rush of the sea into the cove, which carried there large, drifting masses of seaweed, leaving them among the rocks when the tide was out. During the equinoctial winds of the spring and autumn the supply would never fail; and even when the sea was calm, the long, soft, salt-bedewed, trailing masses of the weed, could be gathered there when they could not be found elsewhere for miles along the coast. The task of getting the weed from the breakers was often difficult and dangerous,—so difficult that much of it was left to be carried away by the next incoming tide.

Mally doubtless did not gather half the crop that was there at her feet. What was taken by the returning waves she did not regret; but when interlopers came upon her cove, and gathered her wealth,—her grandfather's wealth, beneath her eyes, then her heart was broken. It was this interloping, this intrusion, that drove poor Mally to the Camelford attorney. But, alas, though the Camelford attorney took Mally's money, he could do nothing for her, and her heart was broken!

She had an idea, in which no doubt her grandfather shared, that the path to the cove was, at any rate, their property. When she was told that the cove, and sea running into the cove, were not the freeholds of her grandfather, she understood that the statement might be true. But what then as to the use of the path? Who had made the path what it was? Had she not painfully, wearily, with exceeding toil, carried up bits of rock with her own little hands, that her grandfather's donkey might have footing for his feet? Had she not scraped together crumbs of earth along the face of the cliff that she might make easier to the animal the track of that rugged way? And now, when she saw big farmers' lads coming down with other donkeys,—and, indeed, there was one who came with a pony; no boy, but a young man, old enough to know better than rob a poor old man and a young girl,—she reviled the whole human race, and swore that the Camelford attorney was a fool.

Any attempt to explain to her that there was still weed enough for her was worse than useless. Was it not all hers and his, or, at any rate, was not the sole way to it his and hers? And was not her trade stopped and impeded? Had she not been forced to back her laden donkey down, twenty yards she said, but it had, in truth, been five, because Farmer Gunliffe's son had been in the way with his thieving pony? Farmer Gunliffe had wanted to buy her weed at his own price, and because she had refused he had set on his thieving son to destroy her in this wicked way.

'I'll hamstring the beast the next time as he's down here!' said Mally to old Glos, while the angry fire literally streamed from her eyes.

Farmer Gunliffe's small homestead—he held about fifty acres of land—was close by the village of Tintagel, and not a mile from the cliff. The sea-wrack, as they call it, was pretty well the only manure within his reach, and no doubt he thought it hard that he should be kept from using it by Mally Trenglos and her obstinacy.

'There's heaps of other coves, Barty,' said Mally to Barty Gunliffe, the farmer's son.

'But none so nigh, Mally, nor yet none that fills 'emselves as this place.'

Then he explained to her that he would not take the weed that came up close to hand. He was bigger than she was, and stronger, and would get it from the outer rocks, with which she never meddled. Then, with scorn in her eye, she swore that she could get it where he durst not venture, and repeated her threat of hamstringing the pony. Barty laughed at her wrath, jeered her because of her wild hair, and called her a mermaid.

'I'll mermaid you!' she cried. 'Mermaid, indeed! I wouldn't be a man to come and rob a poor girl and an old cripple. But you're no man, Barty Gunliffe! You're not half a man.'

Nevertheless, Bartholomew Gunliffe was a very fine young fellow, as far as the eye went. He was about five feet eight inches high, with strong arms and legs, with light curly brown hair and blue eyes. His father was but in a small way as a farmer, but, nevertheless, Barty Gunliffe was well thought of among the girls around. Everybody liked Barty,—excepting only Mally Trenglos, and she hated him like poison.

Barty, when he was asked why so good-natured a lad as he persecuted a poor girl and an old man, threw himself upon the justice of the thing. It wouldn't do at all, according to his view, that any single person should take upon himself to own that which God Almighty sent as the common property of all. He would do Mally no harm, and so he had told her. But Mally was a vixen,—a wicked little vixen; and she must be taught to have a civil tongue in her head. When once Mally would speak him civil as he went for weed, he would get his father to pay the old man some sort of toll for the use of the path.

'Speak him civil?' said Mally. 'Never; not while I have a

tongue in my mouth!' And I fear old Glos encouraged her rather than otherwise in her view of the matter.

But her grandfather did not encourage her to hamstring the pony. Hamstringing a pony would be a serious thing, and old Gloss thought it might be very awkward for both of them if Mally were put into prison. He suggested, therefore, that all manner of impediments should be put in the way of the pony's feet, surmising that the well-trained donkey might be able to work in spite of them. And Barty Gunliffe, on his next descent, did find the passage very awkward when he came near to Malachi's hut, but he made his way down, and poor Mally saw the lumps of rock at which she had laboured so hard pushed on one side or rolled out of the way with a steady persistency of injury towards herself that almost drove her frantic.

'Well, Barty, you're a nice boy,' said old Glos, sitting in the doorway of the hut, as he watched the intruder.

'I ain't a doing no harm to none as doesn't harm me,' said Barty. 'The sea's free to all, Malachi.'

'And the sky's free to all, but I musn't get up on the top of your big barn to look at it,' said Mally, who was standing among the rocks with a long hook in her hand, with which she worked in dragging the weed from the waves. 'But you ain't got no justice nor yet no sperrit, or you wouldn't come here to vex an old man like he.'

'I didn't want to vex him, nor yet to vex you, Mally. You let me be for a while, and we'll be friends yet.'

'Friends!' exclaimed Mally. 'Who'd have the likes of you for a friend? What are you moving them stones for? Them stones belongs to grandfather.' And in her wrath she made a movement as though she were going to fly at him.

'Let him be, Mally,' said the old man; 'let him be. He'll get his punishment. He'll come to be drowned some day if he comes down here when the wind is in shore.'

'That he may be drowned then!' said Mally, in her anger. 'If he was in the big hole there among the rocks, and the sea running in at half tide, I wouldn't lift a hand to help him out.'

'Yes, you would, Mally; you'd fish me up with your hook like a big stick of seaweed.'

She turned from him with scorn as he said this, and went into the hut. It was time for her to get ready for her work, and one of the great injuries done her lay in this,—that such a one as Barty

Gunliffe should come and look at her during her toil among the breakers.

It was an afternoon in April, and the hour was something after four o'clock. There had been a heavy wind from the north-west all the morning, with gusts of rain, and the sea-gulls had been in and out of the cove all the day, which was a sure sign to Mally that the incoming tide would cover the rocks with weed.

The quick waves were now returning over the low reefs, and the time had come at which the treasure must be seized, if it was to be garnered on that day. By seven o'clock it would be growing dark, at nine it would be high water, and before daylight the crop would be carried out again if not collected. All this Mally understood very well, and some of this Barty was beginning to understand also.

As Mally came down with her bare feet, bearing her long hook in her hand, she saw Barty's pony standing patiently on the sand, and in her heart she longed to attack the brute. Barty at this moment, with a common three-pronged fork in his hand, was standing down on a large rock, gazing forth towards the waters. He had declared that he would gather the weed only at places which were inaccessible to Mally, and he was looking out that he might settle where he would begin.

'Let 'un be, let 'un be,' shouted the old man to Mally, as he saw her take a step towards the beast, which she hated almost as much as she hated the man.

Hearing her grandfather's voice through the wind, she desisted from her purpose, if any purpose she had had, and went forth to her work. As she passed down the cove, and scrambled in among the rocks, she saw Barty still standing on his perch; out beyond, the white-curling waves were cresting and breaking themselves with violence, and the wind was howling among the caverns and abutments of the cliff.

Every now and then there came a squall of rain, and though there was sufficient light, the heavens were black with clouds. A scene more beautiful might hardly be found by those who love the glories of the coast.

But neither Mally nor Barty were thinking of such things as these. Indeed they were hardly thinking of their trade after its ordinary forms. Barty was meditating how he might best accomplish his purpose of working beyond the reach of Mally's feminine powers, and Mally was resolving that wherever Barty went she would go farther.

And, in many respects, Mally had the advantage. She knew every rock in the spot, and was sure of those which gave a good foothold, and sure also of those which did not. And then her activity had been made perfect by practice for the purpose to which it was to be devoted. Barty, no doubt, was stronger than she, and quite as active. But Barty could not jump among the waves from one stone to another as she could do, nor was he as yet able to get aid in his work from the very force of the water as she could get it. She had been hunting seaweed in that cove since she had been an urchin of six years old, and she knew every hole and corner and every spot of vantage. The waves were her friends, and she could use them. She could measure their strength, and knew when and where it would cease.

Mally was great down in the salt pools of her own cove,—great, and very fearless. As she watched Barty make his way forward from rock to rock, she told herself, gleefully, that he was going astray. The curl of the wind as it blew into the cove would not carry the weed up to the northern buttresses of the cove; and then there was the great hole just there,—the great hole of which she had spoken when she wished him evil.

And now she went to work, landing many a cargo on the extreme margin of the sand from whence she would be able in the evening to drag it back before the invading waters would return to reclaim the spoil.

And on his side also Barty made his heap up against the northern buttresses of which I have spoken. Barty's heap became big and still bigger, so that he knew, let the pony work as he might, he could not take it all up that evening. But still it was not as large as Mally's heap. Mally's hook was better than his fork, and Mally's skill was better than his strength. And when he failed in some haul Mally would jeer him with a wild, weird laughter, and shriek to him through the wind that he was not half a man. At first he answered her with laughing words, but before long, as she boasted of her success and pointed to his failure, he became angry, and then he answered her no more. He became angry with himself, in that he missed so much of the plunder before him.

The broken sea was full of the long straggling growth which the waves had torn up from the bottom of the ocean, but the masses were carried past him, away from him,—nay, once or twice over him; and then Mally's weird voice would sound in his ear, jeering him. The gloom among the rocks was now becoming thicker and thicker, the tide was beating in with increased strength, and the gusts of wind came with quicker and greater violence. But still he worked on. While Mally worked he would work, and he would work for some time after she was driven in. He would not be beaten by a girl.

The great hole was now full of water, but of water which seemed to be boiling as though in a pot. And the pot was full of floating masses,—large treasures of seaweed which were thrown to and fro upon its surface, but lying there so thick that one would seem almost able to rest upon it without sinking.

Mally knew well how useless it was to attempt to rescue aught from the fury of that boiling cauldron. The hole went in under the rocks, and the side of it towards the shore lay high, slippery, and steep. The hole, even at low water, was never empty; and Mally believed that there was no bottom to it. Fish thrown in there could escape out to the ocean, miles away,—so Mally in her softer moods would tell the visitors to the cove. She knew the hole well. Never did Mally attempt to make her own of weed which had found its way into that pot.

But Barty Gunliffe knew no better, and she watched him as he endeavoured to steady himself on the treacherously slippery edge of the pool. He fixed himself there and made a haul, with some small success. How he managed it she hardly knew, but she stood still for a while watching him anxiously, and then she saw him slip. He slipped, and recovered himself;—slipped again, and again recovered himself.

'Barty, you fool!' she screamed; 'if you get yourself pitched in there, you'll never come out no more.'

Whether she simply wished to frighten him, or whether her heart relented and she had thought of his danger with dismay, who shall say? She could not have told herself. She hated him as much as ever,—but she could hardly have wished to see him drowned before her eyes.

'You go on, and don't mind me,' said he, speaking in a hoarse, angry tone.

'Mind you!—who minds you?' retorted the girl. And then she again prepared herself for her work.

But as she went down over the rocks with her long hook balanced in her hands, she suddenly heard a splash, and, turning quickly round, saw the body of her enemy tumbling amidst the eddying waves in the pool. The tide had now come up so far that every succeeding wave washed into it and over it from the side nearest to the sea, and then ran down again back from the rocks, as the rolling wave receded, with a noise like the fall of a cataract. And then, when the surplus water had retreated for a moment, the surface of the pool would be partly calm, though the fretting bubbles would still boil up and down, and there was ever a simmer on the surface, as though, in truth, the cauldron were heated. But this time of comparative rest was but a moment, for the succeeding breaker would come up almost as soon as the foam of the preceding one had gone, and then again the waters would be dashed upon the rocks, and the sides would echo with the roar of the angry wave.

Instantly Mally hurried across to the edge of the pool, crouching down upon her hands and knees for security as she did so. As a wave receded, Barty's head and face was carried round near to her, and she could see that his forehead was covered with blood. Whether he were alive or dead she did not know. She had seen nothing but his blood, and the light-coloured hair of his head lying amidst the foam. Then his body was drawn along by the suction of the retreating wave; but the mass of water that escaped was not on this occasion large enough to carry the man out with it.

Instantly Mally was at work with her hook, and getting it fixed into his coat, dragged him towards the spot on which she was kneeling. During the half minute of repose she got him so close that she could touch his shoulder. Straining herself down, laying herself over the long bending handle of the hook, she strove to grasp him with her right hand. But she could not do it; she could only touch him.

Then came the next breaker, forcing itself on with a roar, looking to Mally as though it must certainly knock her from her resting-place, and destroy them both. But she had nothing for it but to kneel, and hold by her hook.

The great wave came and rushed over her as she lay almost prostrate, and when the water was gone from her eyes, and the tumult of the foam, and the violence of the roaring breaker had passed by her, she found herself at her length upon the rock, while his body had been lifted up, free from her hook, and was lying upon the slippery ledge, half in the water and half out of it. As she looked at him, in that instant, she could see that his eyes were open and that he was struggling with his hands.

'Hold by the hook, Barty,' she cried, pushing the stick of it before him, while she seized the collar of his coat in her hands.

Had he been her brother, her lover, her father, she could not have clung to him with more of the energy of despair. He did contrive to hold by the stick which she had given him, and when the succeeding wave had passed by, he was still on the ledge. In the next moment she was seated a yard or two above the hole, in comparative safety, while Barty lay upon the rocks with his still bleeding head resting upon her lap.

What could she do now? She could not carry him; and in fifteen minutes the sea would be up where she was sitting. He was quite insensible and very pale, and the blood was coming slowly,—very slowly,—from the wound on his forehead. Ever so gently she put her hand upon his hair to move it back from his face; and then she bent over his mouth to see if he breathed, and as she looked at him she knew that he was beautiful.

What would she not give that he might live? But what could she do? Her grandfather could scarcely get himself down over the rocks, if indeed he could succeed in doing so much as that. Could she drag the wounded man backwards, if it were only a few feet, so that he might lie above the reach of the waves till further assistance could be procured?

She set herself to work and she moved him, almost lifting him. As she did so she wondered at her own strength, but she was very strong at that moment. Slowly, tenderly, falling on the rocks herself so that he might fall on her, she got him back to the margin of the sand, to a spot which the waters would not reach for the next two hours.

Here her grandfather met them, having seen at last what had happened from the door.

'Dada,' she said, 'he fell into the pool yonder, and was battered against the rocks. See there at his forehead.'

'Mally, I'm thinking that he's dead already,' said old Glos, peering down over the body.

'No, dada; he is not dead; but mayhap he's dying. But I'll go at once up to the farm.'

'Mally,' said the old man, 'look at his head. They'll say we murdered him.'

'Who'll say so? Who'll lie like that? Didn't I pull him out of the hole?'

'What matters that? His father'll say we killed him.'

It was manifest to Mally that whatever any one might say here-after, her present course was plain before her. She must run up the path to Gunliffe's farm and get necessary assistance.

So away she went as fast as her naked feet could carry her up the cliff. When at the top she looked round to see if any person might be within ken, but she saw no one. So she ran with all her speed along the headland of the corn-field which led in the direction of old Gunliffe's house, and as she drew near to the homestead she saw that Barty's mother was leaning on the gate. As she approached, she attempted to call, but her breath failed her for any purpose of loud speech, so she ran on till she was able to grasp Mrs Gunliffe by the arm.

'Where's himself?' she said, holding her hand upon her beating heart that she might husband her breath.

'Who is it you mean?' said Mrs Gunliffe, who participated in the family feud against Trenglos and his granddaughter. 'What does the girl clutch me for in that way?'

'He's dying then, that's all.'

'Who is dying? Is it old Malachi? If the old man's bad, we'll send some one down.'

'It ain't dada, it's Barty! Where's himself? where's the master?' But by this time Mrs Gunliffe was in an agony of despair, and was calling out for assistance lustily. Happily Gunliffe, the father, was at hand, and with him a man from the neighbouring village.

'Will you not send for the doctor?' said Mally. 'Oh, man, you should send for the doctor!'

Whether any orders were given for the doctor she did not know, but in a very few minutes she was hurrying across the field again towards the path to the cove, and Gunliffe with the other man and his wife were following her.

As Mally went along she recovered her voice, for their step was not so quick as hers, and that which to them was a hurried move-ment, allowed her to get her breath again. And as she went she tried to explain to the father what had happened, saying but little, however, of her own doings in the matter. The wife hung behind listening, exclaiming every now and again that her boy was killed, and then asking wild questions as to his being yet alive. The father, as he went, said little. He was known as a silent, sober man, well spoken of for diligence and general conduct, but supposed to be stern and very hard when angered.

As they drew near to the top of the path, the other man

whispered something to him, and then he turned round upon Mally and stopped her.

'If he has come by his death between you, your blood shall be taken for his,' said he.

Then the wife shrieked out that her child had been murdered, and Mally, looking round into the faces of the three, saw that her grandfather's words had come true. They suspected her of having taken the life, in saving which she had nearly lost her own.

She looked round at them with awe in her face, and then, without saying a word, preceded them down the path. If they chose to say that she pushed him into the pool, and hit him with her hook as he lay amidst the waters, how could she show that it was not so?

Poor Mally knew little of the law of evidence, and it seemed to her that she was in their hands. But as she went down the steep track with a hurried step,—a step so quick that they could not keep up with her,—her heart was very full,—very full and very high. She had striven for the man's life as though he had been her brother. The blood was yet not dry on her own legs and arms, where she had torn them in his service. At one moment she had felt sure that she would die with him in that pool. And now they said that she had murdered him! It may be that he was not dead, and what would he say if ever he should speak again? Then she thought of that moment when his eyes had opened, and he had seemed to see her. She had no fear for herself, for her heart was very high. But it was full also,—full of scorn, disdain, and wrath.

When she had reached the bottom, she stood close to the door of the hut waiting for them, so that they might precede her to the other group, which was there in front of them, at a little distance on the sand.

'He is there, and dada is with him. Go and look at him,' said Mally.

The father and mother ran on stumbling over the stones, but Mally remained behind by the door of the hut.

Barty Gunliffe was lying on the sand where Mally had left him, and old Malachi Trenglos was standing over him, resting himself with difficulty upon a stick.

'Not a move he's moved since she left him,' said he, 'not a move. I put his head on the old rug as you see, and I tried 'un with a drop of gin, but he wouldn't take it,—he wouldn't take it.'

'Oh, my boy! my boy!' said the mother, throwing herself beside her son upon the sand.

'Haud your tongue, woman,' said the father, kneeling down slowly by the lad's head, 'whimpering that way will do 'un no good.'

Then having gazed for a minute or two upon the pale face beneath him, he looked up sternly into that of Malachi Trenglos. The old man hardly knew how to bear this terrible inquisition.

'He would come,' said Malachi; 'he brought it all upon hisself.'

'Who was it struck him?' said the father.

'Sure he struck hisself, as he fell among the breakers.'

'Liar!' said the father, looking up at the old man.

'They have murdered him!—they have murdered him!' shrieked the mother.

'Haud your peace, woman!' said the husband again. 'They shall give us blood for blood.'

Mally, leaning against the corner of the hovel, heard it all, but did not stir. They might say what they liked. They might make it out to be murder. They might drag her and her grandfather to Camelford Gaol, and then to Bodmin, and the gallows; but they could not take from her the conscious feeling that was her own. She had done her best to save him,—her very best. And she had saved him!

She remembered her threat to him before they had gone down on the rocks together, and her evil wish. Those words had been very wicked; but since that she had risked her life to save his. They might say what they pleased of her, and do what they pleased. She knew what she knew.

Then the father raised his son's head and shoulders in his arms, and called on the others to assist him in carrying Barty towards the path. They raised him between them carefully and tenderly, and lifted their burden on towards the spot at which Mally was standing. She never moved, but watched them at their work; and the old man followed them, hobbling after them with his crutch.

When they had reached the end of the hut she looked upon Barty's face, and saw that it was very pale. There was no longer blood upon the forehead, but the great gash was to be seen there plainly, with its jagged cut, and the skin livid and blue round the orifice. His light brown hair was hanging back, as she had made it to hang when she had gathered it with her hand after the big wave had passed over them. Ah, how beautiful he was in Mally's eyes with that pale face, and the sad scar upon his brow! She turned her face away, that they might not see her tears; but she did not move, nor did she speak.

But now, when they had passed the end of the hut, shuffling along with their burden, she heard a sound which stirred her. She roused herself quickly from her leaning posture, and stretched forth her head as though to listen; then she moved to follow them. Yes, they had stopped at the bottom of the path, and had again laid the body on the rocks. She heard that sound again, as of a long, long sigh, and then, regardless of any of them, she ran to the wounded man's head.

'He is not dead,' she said. 'There; he is not dead.'

As she spoke Barty's eyes opened, and he looked about him.

'Barty, my boy, speak to me,' said the mother.

Barty turned his face upon his mother, smiled, and then stared about him wildly.

'How is it with thee, lad?' said his father. Then Barty turned his face again to the latter voice, and as he did so his eyes fell upon Mally.

'Mally!' he said, 'Mally!'

It could have wanted nothing further to any of those present to teach them that, according to Barty's own view of the case, Mally had not been his enemy; and, in truth, Mally herself wanted no further triumph. That word had vindicated her, and she withdrew back to the hut.

'Dada,' she said, 'Barty is not dead, and I'm thinking they won't say anything more about our hurting him.'

Old Glos shook his head. He was glad the lad hadn't met his death there; he didn't want the young man's blood, but he knew what folk would say.

She would have crept up to the farm if she dared, to ask how Barty was. But her courage failed her when she thought of that, so she went to work again, dragging back the weed she had saved to the spot at which on the morrow she would load the donkey. As she did this she saw Barty's pony still standing patiently under the rock, so she got a lock of fodder and threw it down before the beast.

It had become dark down in the cove, but she was still dragging back the sea-weed, when she saw the glimmer of a lantern coming down the pathway. It was a most unusual sight, for lanterns were not common down in Malachi's Cove. Down came the lantern rather slowly—much more slowly than she was in the habit of descending, and then through the gloom she saw the figure of a man standing at the bottom of the path. She went up to him, and saw that it was Mr Gunliffe, the father.

'Is that Mally?' said Gunliffe.

'Yes, it is Mally; and how is Barty, Mr Gunliffe?'

'You must come to 'un yourself, now at once,' said the farmer. 'He won't sleep a wink till he 's seed you. You must not say but you'll come.'

'Sure I'll come if I'm wanted,' said Mally.

Gunliffe waited a moment, thinking that Mally might have to prepare herself, but Mally needed no preparation. She was dripping with salt water from the weed which she had been dragging, and her elfin locks were streaming wildly from her head; but, such as she was, she was ready.

'Dada's in bed,' she said, 'and I can go now if you please.'

Then Gunliffe turned round and followed her up the path, wondering at the life which this girl led so far away from all her sex. It was now dark night, and he had found her working at the very edge of the rolling waves by herself, in the darkness, while the only human being who might seem to be her protector had already gone to his bed.

When they were at the top of the cliff Gunliffe took her by her hand, and led her along. She did not comprehend this, but she made no attempt to take her hand from his. Something he said about falling on the cliffs, but it was muttered so lowly that Mally hardly understood him. But, in truth, the man knew that she had saved his boy's life, and that he had injured her instead of thanking her. He was now taking her to his heart, and as words were wanting to him, he was showing his love after this silent fashion. He held her by the hand as though she were a child, and Mally tripped along at his side asking him no questions.

When they were at the farm-yard gate, he stopped there for a moment.

'Mally, my girl,' he said, 'he'll not be content till he sees thee, but thou must not stay long wi' him, lass. Doctor says he's weak like, and wants sleep badly.'

Mally merely nodded her head, and then they entered the house. Mally had never been within it before, and looked about with wondering eyes at the furniture of the big kitchen. But she did not pause here a moment, but was led up to the bedroom above stairs, where Barty was lying on his mother's bed.

'Is it Mally herself?' said the voice of the weak youth.

'It's Mally herself,' said the mother, 'so now you can say what you please.'

'Mally,' said he, 'Mally, it's along of you that I'm alive this moment.'

'I'll not forget it on her,' said the father, with his eyes turned away from her. 'I'll never forget it on her.'

'We hadn't a one but only him,' said the mother, with her apron up to her face.

'Mally, you'll be friends with me now?' said Barty.

To have been made lady of the manor of the cove for ever, Mally couldn't have spoken a word now. It was not only that the words and presence of the people there cowed her and made her speechless, but the big bed, and the looking-glass, and the unheard-of wonders of the chamber, made her feel her own insignificance. But she crept up to Barty's side, and put her hand upon his.

'I'll come and get the weed, Mally; but it shall all be for you,' said Barty.

'Indeed, you won't then, Barty dear,' said the mother; 'you'll never go near the awesome place again. What would we do if you were took from us?'

'He mustn't go near the hole if he does,' said Mally, speaking at last in a solemn voice, and imparting the knowledge which she had kept to herself while Barty was her enemy; ' 'specially not if the wind's any way from the nor'ard.'

'She'd better go down now,' said the father.

Barty kissed the hand which he held, and Mally, looking at him as he did so, thought that he was like an angel.

'You'll come and see us to-morrow, Mally,' said he.

To this she made no answer, but followed Mrs Gunliffe out of the room. When they were down in the kitchen, the mother had tea for her, and thick milk, and a hot cake,—all the delicacies which the farm could afford.

'I'll never forget it on her—never,' the father had said.

Those words stuck to her from that moment, and seemed to sound in her ears all the night. How glad she was that Barty had come down to the cove,—oh, yes, how glad! There was no question of his dying now, and as for the blow on his forehead, what harm was that to a lad like him?

'But father shall go with you,' said Mrs Gunliffe, when Mally prepared to start for the cove by herself. Mally, however, would not hear of this. She could find her way to the cove whether it was light or dark.

'Mally, thou art my child now, and I shall think of thee so,' said the mother, as the girl went off by herself.

I need not, I think, tell the tale any further. That Mally did become Mrs Gunliffe's child, and how she became so the reader will understand; and in process of time the big kitchen and all the wonders of the farm-house were her own. The people said that Barty Gunliffe had married a mermaid out of the sea; but when it was said in Mally's hearing I doubt whether she liked it; and when Barty himself would call her a mermaid she would frown at him, and throw about her black hair, and pretend to cuff him with her little hand.

Old Glos was brought up to the top of the cliff, and lived his few remaining days under the roof of Mr Gunliffe's house; and as for the cove and the right of sea-weed, from that time forth all that has been supposed to attach itself to Gunliffe's farm, and I do not know that any of the neighbours are prepared to dispute the right.

George Lambert and Miss P.

George Lambert was a man who liked to take holidays, and circumstances combined to gratify his taste. Though a spasmodic worker, needing long periods of relaxation, he possessed in the field of electrical engineering such brilliant and profitable talents that his firm, besides paying him an ample salary, readily allowed him frequent leave. He had no wife to double expenses, and he had a secretary to save him all trouble. Miss Parker, (always referred to by George as My Miss P.), bought tickets, made reservations, told him which 'plane he was catching and whether he should pack a dinner-jacket; and had moreover, in the course of their association, developed such a remarkable nose for hotels that George was never let down at his destination. Give Miss P. half-a-dozen identically lyrical brochures, and she would unerringly pick out that which most closely approximated the reality. If Miss P. promised George there would be dancing, there was dancing—and to a first-class orchestra; if she assured him the cuisine would be genuine Provençal, George battened on *tarte aux oignons*. Her powers of divination extended even over the weather: if she told George there would be snow, there was. Miss P. herself never ventured further than Dorset, to a summer camp; had George ever thought about it he would have assumed that she enjoyed packing him off to Sweden or Majorca or the Canaries—always by the best route and to the best hotel—simply as an exercise in virtuosity.

As a matter of fact, Miss P. was so completely invaluable to George that he never thought about her at all. He paid her, or rather his firm paid her, an evidently adequate salary, and in return Miss P. (besides organizing his holidays) did all George's routine work, deciphered his scrawls, saw his drawings through the print-room, provided doughnuts for his tea, and dropped an iron curtain over his meditations. George simply found conditions tolerable. He had never had to do without Miss P., because she always took her holiday while he was taking one of his.

None the less, as he sat dining on the terrace of the Rosario, George Lambert spared Miss P. a grateful thought. Hotel and grounds occupied almost the total area of a small Mediterranean island, and the situation was superb. Wherever the eye turned blue sky met blue sea, broken only by the green and rose, or green and gold, of oleanders and orange-trees. The building itself was washed a dim, tactful pink. There was a bath to every room, and the food was as perfectly simple as money could buy. Moreover—George was something of a holiday philanderer—George had already marked, at a table not far from his own, a charming little creature as solitary as himself.

Miss P. had assured him there would be dancing: there was. The twanging mandolins were first-class of their kind, and in the situation not to be improved on. In plain English—George always found this the best approach—he invited the charming little creature to dance. She accepted. She was Italian, she was a Contessa, she had a disagreeable old husband in Rome; so far George's plain English (hers was prettily broken), took him that first night; he went to bed extremely pleased with himself, with the Rosario, and with Miss P.

He did not feel nearly so pleased when the following afternoon, coming up from the diving-rocks, he met Miss P. coming down.

He almost failed to recognize her; it would have been excusable. In the office Miss P. always wore black or navy-blue, high-collared with white. She now wore a bright yellow bikini. In the office Miss P. always wore glasses; she did still, but they were the universal sun-glasses of the coast. No wonder George stared. No wonder that for some seconds he doubted his eyes. When he looked at Miss P.'s navel, he disbelieved them altogether. In fact, as he went on up the path, he decided he'd been mistaken.

By evening, however, he could deceive himself no longer. Dressed for dinner, in neat and appropriate organdy, white with navy trimmings, Miss P. was unarguably Miss P. She sat at a table for one, apparently enjoying both her dinner and the view; she looked very comfortable. George, on the other hand, was beginning to realize why his sub-conscious had fought so hard not to recognize her. There are times when a man wants his secretary around, and times when he doesn't. Consuming melon, George felt merely surprised; he also—a kindly chap at heart—feared Miss P. might be going to find herself a trifle lonely and out of things. But when the mandolins struck up after dinner, when he led his Contessa on to the dance floor, the full realization burst on him that Miss P. was going to be a damned nuisance.

There are times when a man wants his secretary around, and times when he doesn't. The moment when a Contessa's cheek lightly brushes his own is a time when he doesn't. The charming little creature, her gesture made, naturally awaited an answering pressure from George's arm. They were just passing Miss P.'s table. Of course George didn't give a darn what Miss P. thought of him, it was no business of hers, but her mere presence—trailing, so to speak, clouds of office memoranda—put him off his stroke. The Contessa pouted. 'Let's go into the garden,' said George. The Contessa shook her head. He shouldn't have said it till later. They finished the dance in silence, and the Contessa devoted the rest of her evening to a racing motorist. George had to hang about until after midnight, when Miss P. went to bed, before he could even begin to make up lost ground.

George didn't sleep very well that night, because he was thinking about Miss P.

By morning he was ready to take action. How often a problem needs only to be stated, to be solved! George knew, vaguely, that Miss P.'s holiday commonly lasted a fortnight. If she was going to spend the entire two weeks at the Rosario, George's own holiday would be ruined. But so—how could the solution have evaded him so long?—so would Miss P. The Rosario was quite fantastically expensive. However adequately salaried, Miss P. couldn't possibly afford it, her instinct for the best was obviously leading her into terrible difficulties. She wouldn't be able to pay. The hotel would fetch the police. Miss P. would be incarcerated, possibly for months, in some unhygienic island jail. It was George's plain duty to save her from this fate.

He was glad to find her with a beach-robe over her bikini. The decorous white towelling made her look more like his Miss P. With the kindest, if not the most disinterested intentions, George approached.

'Well, this is a surprise!' said George heartily.

'*Is*n't it?' agreed Miss P.

'I thought you always went to Dorset,' said George.

'I always *have*,' agreed Miss P. 'But just for once I thought I'd like to see one of the places *you* go to.'

George was touched. He might have gone on being touched had not Miss P. seen fit at that moment to cast aside her robe. She had quite a good figure, and she couldn't have been more than twenty-five. The Contessa, just then passing, cut George dead.

'I'm only a bit worried,' said George, 'about what it may be letting you in for. Financially, I mean. I mean, I don't know exactly what the firm pays you, but I do know what the Rosario costs—'

'The earth,' said Miss P.

'Exactly,' said George. 'I mean, I'm sure you can't afford it. I'm sure there are dozens of nice little *pensions* round Amalfi where you'd be much happier. You've probably booked your room here, but if you'd like me to talk to the manager—'

'I shall be able to pay,' said Miss P.

'Honestly,' said George, 'I don't see how you can.'

Miss P. gave him a very strange look.

'Wait till the auditors check the petty cash,' said Miss P.

George was so taken aback, George was so horrified and alarmed, that he simply sat where he was, mouth and eyes agape, while Miss P. rather gracefully rose and strolled down to the swimming-beach. He continued to sit and gape for several minutes after she disappeared. He had never been so upset in all his life.

If he hadn't heard the words from Miss P.'s own lips, George would never have believed them. If the whole office, if the whole Metropolitan Police Force, had accused Miss P. of pocketing the petty cash, George wouldn't have believed *them*. A bishop pocketing the collection was less unlikely to him. Only by Miss P.'s own statement—and the very peculiar look accompanying it—could his trust in her have been shaken.

To make matters worse, he didn't know what the devil to do. Should he wire the office, and tell them to check the petty cash at once? How much was there ever *in* the petty cash? His notions of office procedure were so vague that he couldn't even guess the answer. Had Miss P. made off with fifty pounds, or a hundred? If fifty, George thought, he'd pay up out of his own pocket, just to save trouble all round. But suppose it was a hundred? Suppose it was more? Suppose the firm prosecuted? Suppose Miss P.'s jail wasn't after all the island variety, but Holloway? 'The girl's *mad* ...' thought George.

He decided, however, not to wire. (He was always lazy: and he could hardly get Miss P. to wire for him.) He decided to make one more attempt to bring her to her senses.

'Look here,' said George that night, in the course of a rhumba, 'why don't you clear out to Amalfi as I've suggested, save whatever you've snaffled, and put it back before anyone finds out?'

'I want to see life,' said Miss P.

George released her for two stamping steps. He'd had to ask her to dance because she'd picked up with some Poles, and it was the only way of getting her alone.

'You'll get the sack, you know,' said George.

'At least I'll have seen life first,' said Miss P.

She was impossible. She was completely unreasonable. She also stayed on at the Rosario. For George in the end followed the line of least resistance, and did nothing. He decided to let Miss P. take whatever was coming to her, but in due course. If the only way of eliminating Miss P. from the Rosario was to have her flown back to England in custody, he decided to put up with Miss P.

Of course his own holiday was shot to pieces. It wasn't that Miss P. in any way kept tabs on George, on the contrary—and how naturally—she tended to avoid him. Nor was her general behaviour in any sense a reproach to his own—on the contrary again: as the days went by Miss P. picked up with more and more dubious characters, and freely entered into their fun and games. She certainly wasn't lonely, she certainly wasn't out of things; at the cocktail-hour one couldn't see Miss P. for Greeks. ('Because she's a free spender,' thought George censoriously. 'They probably think she's a millionairess . . .') But the odd result was that as the conduct of Miss P. became more abandoned, so the conduct of George became more restrained. He felt, obscurely, that he ought to set her an example: he meant *his* behaviour to reproach *hers*: naturally his holiday was ruined.

Instead of pursuing the Contessa, he got into a steady, all-male bridge four. Instead of going to bed at dawn, he retired in good order at midnight. He played a lot of tennis with the pro., and helped coach a couple of small boys. He taught a female infant to swim. In no time at all every child in the hotel was addressing him as Uncle George. None of it had the least effect on Miss P.

Obviously George couldn't tell how she would have behaved *without* his example, he only felt she could hardly have behaved worse. (He thought about her almost continuously.) Her particular ally was an Italian, lithe and smiling, superb on the diving-board, and given to full-throated song in the small hours of the morning. He used to serenade Miss P. regularly. There was also a Greek who taught her poker, and a Pole who taught her Polish. Miss P.'s days were filled to overflowing, and as for her nights . . . well, everyone hoped she got enough sleep. But she was certainly seeing life:

her skin browned and her hair bleached, her figure got better and better, her spirits rose higher and higher, and she was known as the Blonde Bombshell.

At the end of ten days George cut his holiday short and went home. He had lost a good deal of money at bridge, he had tennis-elbow, and he was sick of being called Uncle George. He said good-bye to Miss P. only by accident; they happened to meet on the landing-stage.

'You're not *going*!' exclaimed Miss P., in surprise.

'Yes, I am,' said George.

'But you've still four days,' said Miss P. automatically.

'And I'm still going,' said George.

'Oh, well,' said Miss P. lightly, 'I expect one of the typists will look after you. Ask for Mabel.'

It was a slight return to grace—but how slight! Never before had she abandoned him, even for twenty-four hours, to the mercy of the typists. Never before had George returned from a holiday uncertain of finding Miss P. there before him. How could she now abandon him to Mabel? And in a wider sense, how *could* she? How could she speak so insouciantly, stand so insouciantly, browned and bleached and bikini'd, knowing what lay in store? 'I could understand her not worrying about me if she was worrying about herself,' thought George, 'but dammit, she doesn't seem to be worrying at all! *I'm* the one who's worrying ...'

Once again George stared at her in amazement; and once again Miss P. gave him that strange, disturbing look. They stood thus for perhaps half a minute, neither speaking again; then someone shouted from the gangway, and George turned and walked up it.

He was to fly from Nice; Miss P. had assured him—only a fort-night ago—but how much can happen in a fortnight!—that this was far the best route.

As soon as George got back to the office he demanded an audit of the petty cash. It wasn't the right time and he could give no sensible reason, he simply said he was a bit worried about some-thing; but he persisted, and he was invaluable, so they humoured him.

There wasn't a penny missing.

A couple of months later George Lambert told the whole story to a woman he was rather fond of. Mrs Cornish listened with great interest, and at the end laughed.

'My dear George,' said Mrs Cornish, 'it's as plain as the nose on your face. Miss P.'s in love with you.'

George was astounded.

'She wanted you to *notice* her,' explained Mrs Cornish. 'I don't suppose you ever noticed her in the office, you just took her for granted. So she followed you to the Rosario—'

'But it doesn't make sense,' interrupted George. 'Even if you were right, as I jolly well know you're not—why did she tell that thumping lie? It worried me no end.'

'She *wanted* you to worry,' elaborated Mrs Cornish patiently. 'Of course it makes sense. On your own showing, you spent your entire time noticing, and thinking about, and worrying over Miss P. You noticed she's got a good figure—'

'Very,' said George.

'—which you'd never noticed before, and you noticed that other men were attracted to her—'

'Because she bought them drinks.'

'Fiddle,' said Mrs Cornish. 'I've no doubt there were other women in the hotel prepared to be just as generous. *They* weren't known as Blonde Bombshells.'

George thought back.

'She did,' he admitted, 'look pretty striking in that bikini. And certainly I noticed her. But your theory still doesn't make sense.'

'Of course it does,' retorted Mrs Cornish. 'Why don't you marry her, George? She sounds as though she'd make you a first-rate wife.'

George rather glumly emptied his tea-cup.

'She's married someone else,' said George. 'I'm trying to tell you. She left a month ago to marry this Italian chap. They're going to run an hotel. If *that* doesn't make your theory nonsense, I don't know what does.'

'Dear me,' said Mrs Cornish.

'You tell me she's in love with me,' persisted George, 'and she goes and marries an Italian. The office gave 'em a tea-set. What have you to say to that?'

Mrs Cornish reflected a moment. She did indeed look surprised, but her expression was changing fast. She finally, George thought resentfully, looked rather pleased.

'At least Miss P.'s holiday wasn't wasted,' said Mrs Cornish. 'All's well that ends well, don't you think?'

'No, I don't,' said George. 'It hasn't ended well at all, I'm still absolutely baffled, and what's worse, I've got to find another secretary.'

Mrs Cornish laughed and laughed. She laughed so long that George grew impatient.

'It's not so easy as you think,' he complained, 'to find someone who remembers the doughnuts.'

Stephen Vincent Benét

Too Early Spring

I'm writing this down because I don't ever want to forget the way
it was. It doesn't seem as if I could, now, but they all tell you things
change. And I guess they're right. Older people must have forgotten or they couldn't be the way they are. And that goes for even
the best ones, like Dad and Mr Grant. They try to understand
but they don't seem to know how. And the others make you feel
dirty or else they make you feel stupid. Till, pretty soon, you begin
to forget yourself—you begin to think, 'Well, maybe they're right
and it was that way.' And that's the end of everything. So I've
got to write this down. Because they smashed it for ever—but it
wasn't the way they said.

I don't quite know where the beginning was. We had a good
summer, but it was just the same summer. I worked pretty hard
at the jackknife. I'll never dive like my older brother, Kerry, but
you want to be as all-around as you can. And, when I took my
measurements, at the end of the summer, I was 5 ft 9¾ and I'd
gained 12 lbs. 6 oz. That isn't bad for going on sixteen and the old
chest expansion was O.K. You don't want to get too heavy, because
basketball's a fast game, but the year before was the year when
I got my height, and I was so skinny, I got tired.

It sounds as if I were trying to run away from what I have to
write down, but I'm not. I want to remember that summer, too,
because it's the last happy one I'll ever have. Oh, when I'm an
old man—thirty or forty—things may be all right again. But that's
a long time to wait and it won't be the same.

And yet, that summer was different, too, in a way. So it must
have started then, though I didn't know it. I went around with
the gang as usual and we had a good time. But, every now and
then it would strike me we were acting like awful kids. They
thought I was getting the big head, but I wasn't. It just wasn't
much fun—even going to the cave. It was like going on shooting
marbles when you're in high school.

I was sitting alone one night by the lake—right down by the
edge of the water. There was a big moon. It's funny how you can
be unhappy and nobody knows it but yourself.

I was thinking about Sheila Coe. She's Kerry's girl. They fight but they get along. She's awfully pretty and she can swim like a fish. Once she and I had a long talk alone. She was fine. And she didn't pull any of this big sister stuff, either, the way some girls will with a fellow's brother.

And when the canoe came along, by the edge of the lake, I thought for a moment it was her. I thought maybe she was looking for Kerry and maybe she'd stop and talk to me again. I don't know why I thought that—I didn't have any reason. Then I saw it was just the Sharon kid, with a new kind of hair-do that made her look grown-up, and I felt sore. She didn't have any business out on the lake at her age. She was just a sophomore in high school, the same as me.

I chunked a stone in the water and it splashed right by the canoe, but she didn't squeal. She just said 'Fish', and chuckled. It struck me it was a kid's trick, trying to scare a kid.

'Hello, Helen,' I said. 'Where did you swipe the canoe?'

'It's an old one,' she said. 'I'm not supposed to have it out at night. But you won't tell anybody, will you?'

'Be your age,' I said. 'I'll paddle awhile, if you want,' I said.

'All right,' she said, so she brought it in and I got aboard. She went back in the bow and I took the paddle. I'm not strong on carting kids around, as a rule. But it was better than sitting there by myself.

'Where do you want to go?' I said.

'Oh, back towards the house,' she said in a shy kind of voice. 'I ought to, really.'

'O.K.,' I said. I didn't paddle fast, just let her slip. There was a lot of moon on the water. She was a sensible kid, she didn't ask fool questions or giggle about nothing at all.

I took quite a shine to her and we talked. The Sharons have only been in town three years and somehow I'd never really noticed her before. Mrs Sharon's awfully good-looking but she and Mr Sharon fight. That's hard on a kid. And she was a quiet kid.

She had a small kind of face and her eyes were sort of like a kitten's. You could see she got a great kick out of pretending to be grown-up—and yet it wasn't all pretending. A couple of times I felt just as if I were talking to Sheila Coe. Only more comfortable, because, after all, we were the same age.

Do you know, after we put the canoe up, I walked all the way back home, around the lake? And most of the way, I ran. I felt swell, too. I felt as if I could run for ever and not stop. It was like finding something. I hadn't imagined anybody could ever feel the way I did about some things. And here was another person, even if it was a girl.

I didn't see her again till we were both back in high school. Mr Sharon's uncle died, back east. They went to the funeral and stayed a few weeks. All that time, I kept remembering that night and her little face. If I'd seen her in daylight, first, it might have been different. No, it wouldn't have been.

I wasn't thinking of her when we bumped into each other, the first day of school. It was raining and she had on a green raincoat and her hair was curly under her hat. We grinned and said hello and had to run. But something happened to us, I guess.

I'll say this now—it wasn't like Tot Pickens and Mabel Palmer. It wasn't like Junior Davis and Betty Page—though they've been going together ever since kindergarten. It wasn't like any of those things. We didn't get sticky and sloppy. It wasn't like going with a girl.

There'd been days and days when we'd hardly see each other, except in class, I had basketball practice almost every afternoon and sometimes evenings and she was taking music lessons four times a week. But you don't have to be always twos-ing with a person, if you feel that way about them. You seem to know the way they're thinking and feeling, the way you know yourself.

She had that little face and the eyes like a kitten's. When it rained, her hair curled all over the back of her neck. Her hair was yellow. She wasn't a tall girl but she wasn't chunky—just light and well made and quick. She was awfully alive without being nervous—she never bit her fingernails or chewed the end of her pencil, but she'd answer quicker than anyone in the class. Nearly everybody liked her, but she wasn't best friends with any special girl, the mushy way they get. The teachers all thought a lot of her, even Miss Eagles. Well, I had to spoil that.

If we'd been like Tot and Mabel, we could have had a lot more time together, I guess. But Helen isn't a liar and I'm not a snake. It wasn't easy, going over to her house, because Mr and Mrs Sharon would be polite to each other in front of you and yet there'd be something wrong. And she'd have to be fair to both of them and they were always pulling at her. But we'd look at each other across the table and then it would be all right.

I don't know when it was that we knew we'd get married to

each other, some time. We just started talking about it, one day, as if we always had. We were sensible, we knew it couldn't happen right off. We thought maybe when we were eighteen. That was two years but we knew we had to be educated. You don't get as good a job, if you aren't.

We weren't mushy either, like some people. We got to kissing each other goodbye, sometimes, because that's what you do when you're in love. It was cool, the way she kissed you, it was like leaves. But lots of the time we wouldn't even talk about getting married, we'd just play checkers or go over the old homework, or once in a while go to the movies with the gang.

It was really a wonderful winter. I played in every basketball game and she'd sit in the stands and watch and I'd know she was there. You could see her little green hat or her yellow hair.

And it's a queer thing; but everybody seemed to be pleased. That's what I can't get over. They liked to see us together. The grown people, I mean. Even Mother was all right, though she didn't like Mrs Sharon.

But it wasn't so nice for us after the spring came.

Usually basketball's over by the time spring really breaks, but this year it hit us while we still had three games to play. And it certainly messed us up as a team. After Bladesbury nearly licked us, Mr Grant, the coach, called off all practice till the day before the St Matthew's game. He knew we were stale—and they'd been state champions two years. They'd have walked all over us, the way we were going.

The first thing I did was telephone Helen. Because that meant there were six extra afternoons we could have, if she could get rid of her music lessons. Well, she said, wasn't it wonderful, her music teacher had a cold? And that seemed just like Fate.

Well, that was a great week and we were so happy. We went to the movies five times and once Mrs Sharon let us take her little car. She was funny—sometimes she'd be awfully kind and friendly to you and sometimes she'd be like a piece of dry ice. She was that way with Mr Sharon, too. But it was a wonderful ride. We got stuff out of the kitchen and drove way out in the country. And we found an old house, with the windows gone, on top of a hill, and parked the car and took the stuff up to the house and ate it there. There weren't any chairs or tables but we pretended there were.

We pretended it was our house, after we were married. I'll never forget that. She even brought paper napkins and paper plates and she set two places on the floor.

'Well, Charles,' she said, sitting opposite me, with her feet tucked under, 'I don't suppose you remember the days we were both in school.'

'Sure,' I said—she was always much quicker pretending things than I was—'I remember them all right. That was before Tot Pickens got to be President.' And we both laughed.

'It seems very distant in the past to me—we've been married so long,' she said, as if she really believed it. She looked at me.

'Would you mind turning off the TV, dear?' she said. 'That music always gets on my nerves.'

I went and turned it off. Then she lowered her eyes a minute, just like her mother, and pushed away her plate.

'I'm not very hungry tonight,' she said. 'You won't mind if I go upstairs?'

'Aw, don't be like that,' I said. It was too much like her mother.

'I was just seeing if I could,' she said. 'But I never will, Chuck.'

'I'll never tell you you're nervous, either,' I said. 'I—oh, gosh!'

She grinned and it was all right. 'Mr Ashland and I have never had a serious argument in our wedded lives,' she said.

'Say, what kind of a house have we got?'

'It's a lovely house,' she said. 'We've got TV sets in every room. We've got a regular movie projector. There's always something in the refrigerator. You've got lots of clothes and dogs. You smell of pipes and being out in the open.'

'I wish I had a dog,' I said. 'It's a long time since Jack died.'

'Oh, Chuck, I'm sorry,' she said.

'Oh, that's all right,' I said. 'He was getting old and his ear was always bothering him. But he was a good dog. Go ahead.'

'Well,' she said, 'of course we give parties—'

'Cut the parties,' I said.

'Chuck! They're grand ones!'

'I'm a homebody,' I said. 'Give me—er—my wife and my little family and—say, how many kids have we got, anyhow?'

She counted on her fingers. 'Seven.'

'Good Lord,' I said.

'Well, I always wanted seven. You make it three, if you like.'

I held her for a long while. It was like holding something awfully valuable. It wasn't mushy or that way. I know what that's like, too.

'It takes so long to get old,' she said. 'I wish I could grow up tomorrow. I wish we both could.'

'Don't you worry,' I said. 'It's going to be all right.'

We didn't say much, going back in the car, but we were happy enough. I thought we passed Miss Eagles, one of our teachers, at the turn. That worried me a little. But, after all, Mrs Sharon had said we could take the car.

We wanted to go back again, after that, but it was too far to walk and that was the only time we had the car.

That St Matthew's game was a game! We beat them 66–64 and it took an extra period and I thought it would never end. The two-goal lead they had looked as big as the Rocky Mountains all the first half. And they gave me a full school cheer when we tied them up. You don't forget things like that.

Afterwards Father and Mother had to go to some party. I didn't mind. But, all the same, when I'd said goodnight to them and gone into the house, I felt sort of let down.

I knew I'd be tired the next day but I didn't feel sleepy yet. I was too excited. I wanted to talk to somebody. So I thought I'd call up Helen and then I thought—probably she's asleep and Mrs Sharon will answer the phone and be sore. And then I thought— well, anyhow, I could go over and walk around the block and look at her house. I'd get some fresh air out of it, anyway, and it would be a little like seeing her.

So I did—and it was a swell night—cool and a lot of stars— and I felt like a king, walking over. All the lower part of the Sharon house was dark but a window upstairs was lit. I knew it was her window. I went around back of the driveway and whistled once— the whistle we made up. I never expected her to hear.

But she did, and there she was at the window, smiling. She made motions that she'd come down to the side door.

Honestly, it took my breath away when I saw her. She had on a kind of yellow thing over her night clothes and she looked so pretty. Her feet were so pretty in those slippers. I know I oughtn't to have gone into the house. But we didn't think anything about it—we were just glad to see each other. We hadn't had any sort of chance to talk over the game.

We sat in front of the fire in the living room and she went out to the kitchen and got us cookies and milk. I wasn't really hungry, but it was like that time at the house, eating with her. Mr and Mrs Sharon were out at a party, too, so we weren't bothering them or anything. We turned off the lights because there was plenty of light from the fire.

It was quiet and lovely and the firelight made shadows on the ceiling. We talked a lot and then we just sat, each of us knowing the other was there. And the room got quieter and quieter and I'd told her about the game and I didn't feel excited or jumpy any more—just rested and happy. And then I knew by her breathing that she was asleep and I put my arm around her for just a minute. I was going to wake her in a minute. I didn't realize how tired I was myself.

And then we were back in that house in the country and it was our home and we ought to have been happy. But something was wrong because there still wasn't any glass in the windows and a wind kept blowing through them and we tried to shut the doors but they wouldn't shut. We were both running through the house, trying to shut the doors, and we were cold and afraid. Then the sun rose outside the windows, burning and yellow and so big it covered the sky. And with the sun was a horrible, weeping voice. It was Mrs Sharon saying, 'Oh, my God, oh, my God.'

I didn't know what had happened, for a minute when I woke. And then I did and it was awful. Mrs Sharon was saying, 'Oh, Helen—I trusted you . . .' and looking as if she were going to faint. And Mr Sharon looked at her for a minute and his face was horrible. Then he said to Helen—

I don't want to think of what they said. I don't want to think of any of the things they said. Mr Sharon is a bad man. And she is a bad woman, even if she is Helen's mother. All the same, I could stand the things he said better than hers.

I don't want to think of any of it. And it is all spoiled now. Everything is spoiled. Miss Eagles saw us going to that house in the country and she said terrible things. They made Helen sick and she hasn't been back at school. There isn't any way I can see her. And if I could, it would be spoiled. We'd be thinking about the things they said.

I don't know how many of the people know, at school. But Tot Pickens passed me a note. And, that afternoon, I caught him behind his house. I'd have broken his nose if they hadn't pulled me off. I meant to. Mother cried when she heard about it and Dad took me into his room and talked to me. He said you can't lick the whole town. But I will anybody like Tot Pickens.

Dad and Mother have been all right. But they say things about

Helen and that's almost worse. They're for me because I'm their son. But they don't understand.

I just go to school and back now. They want me to go with the gang, the way I did, but I can't do that. Not after Tot. Of course my marks are a lot better because I've got more time to study now. But it's lucky I haven't got Miss Eagles though Dad made her apologize.

I think Mr Grant knows because he asked me to his house once and we had a talk. Not about that, though I was afraid he would.

But we got to talking, somehow, about history and things like that and how things had changed. Why, there were kings and queens who got married younger than Helen and me. Only now we lived longer and had a lot more to learn. So it couldn't happen now. 'It's civilization,' he said. 'And all civilization's got against nature. But I suppose we've got to have it. Only sometimes it isn't easy.' Well, somehow or other, that made me feel less lonely. Before that I'd been feeling that I was the only person on earth who'd ever felt that way.

They're going to send Helen away to a school for girls. I found that out. Maybe they'll let me see her before she goes. But, if we do, it will be all wrong and in front of people and everybody pretending. I sort of wish they don't—though I want to, terribly. When her mother took her upstairs that night—she wasn't the same Helen. She looked at me as if she was afraid of me. And no matter what they do for us now, they can't fix that.

The Gift of the Magi

One dollar and eighty-seven cents. That was all. And sixty cents of it was in pennies. Pennies saved one and two at a time by bulldozing the grocer and the vegetable man and the butcher until one's cheek burned with the silent imputation of parsimony that such close dealing implied. Three times Della counted it. One dollar and eighty-seven cents. And the next day would be Christmas.

There was clearly nothing left to do but flop down on the shabby little couch and howl. So Della did it. Which instigates the moral reflection that life is made up of sobs, sniffles, and smiles, with sniffles predominating.

While the mistress of the home is gradually subsiding from the first stage to the second, take a look at the home. A furnished flat at $8 per week. It did not exactly beggar description, but it certainly had that word on the look-out for the mendicancy squad.

In the vestibule below was a letter-box into which no letter would go, and an electric button from which no mortal finger could coax a ring. Also appertaining thereunto was a card bearing the name 'Mr James Dillingham Young'.

The 'Dillingham' had been flung to the breeze during a former period of prosperity when its possessor was being paid $30 per week. Now, when the income was shrunk to $20, the letters of 'Dillingham' looked blurred, as though they were thinking seriously of contracting to a modest and unassuming D. But whenever Mr. James Dillingham Young came home and reached his flat above he was called 'Jim' and greatly hugged by Mrs James Dillingham Young, already introduced to you as Della. Which is all very good.

Della finished her cry and attended to her cheeks with the powder rag. She stood by the window and looked out dully at a grey cat walking a grey fence in a grey backyard. To-morrow would be Christmas Day, and she had only $1.87 with which to buy Jim a present. She had been saving every penny she could for months, with this result. Twenty dollars a week doesn't go far. Expenses had been greater than she had calculated. They always are. Only $1.87 to buy a present for Jim. Her Jim. Many a happy hour she had spent planning for something nice for him. Something fine and rare and sterling—something just a little bit near to being worthy of the honour of being owned by Jim.

There was a pier-glass between the windows of the room. Perhaps you have seen a pier-glass in an $8 flat. A very thin and very agile person may, by observing his reflection in a rapid sequence of longitudinal strips, obtain a fairly accurate conception of his looks. Della, being slender, had mastered the art.

Suddenly she whirled from the window and stood before the glass. Her eyes were shining brilliantly, but her face had lost its colour within twenty seconds. Rapidly she pulled down her hair and let it fall to its full length.

Now, there were two possessions of the James Dillingham Youngs in which they both took a mighty pride. One was Jim's gold watch that had been his father's and his grandfather's. The other was Della's hair. Had the Queen of Sheba lived in the flat across the airshaft, Della would have let her hair hang out the window some day to dry just to depreciate Her Majesty's jewels and gifts. Had King Solomon been the janitor, with all his treasures piled up in the basement, Jim would have pulled out his watch every time he passed, just to see him pluck at his beard from envy.

So now Della's beautiful hair fell about her, rippling and shining like a cascade of brown waters. It reached below her knee and made itself almost a garment for her. And then she did it up again nervously and quickly. Once she faltered for a minute and stood still while a tear or two splashed on the worn red carpet.

On went her old brown jacket; on went her old brown hat. With a whirl of skirts and with the brilliant sparkle still in her eyes, she fluttered out of the door and down the stairs to the street.

Where she stopped the sign read: 'Mme Sofronie. Hair Goods of All Kinds.' One flight up Della ran, and collected herself, panting. Madame, large, too white, chilly, hardly looked the 'Sofronie.'

'Will you buy my hair?' asked Della.

'I buy hair,' said Madame. 'Take yer hat off and let's have a sight at the looks of it.'

Down rippled the brown cascade.

'Twenty dollars,' said Madame, lifting the mass with a practised hand.

'Give it to me quick,' said Della.

Oh, and the next two hours tripped by on rosy wings. Forget

the hashed metaphor. She was ransacking the stores for Jim's present.

She found it at last. It surely had been made for Jim and no one else. There was no other like it in any of the stores, and she had turned all of them inside out. It was a platinum watch chain simple and chaste in design, properly proclaiming its value by substance alone and not by meretricious ornamentation—as all good things should do. It was even worthy of The Watch. As soon as she saw it she knew that it must be Jim's. It was like him. Quietness and value—the description applied to both. Twenty-one dollars they took from her for it, and she hurried home with the eighty-seven cents. With that chain on his watch Jim might be properly anxious about the time in any company. Grand as the watch was, he sometimes looked at it on the sly on account of the old leather strap that he used in place of a chain.

When Della reached home her intoxication gave way a little to prudence and reason. She got out her curling irons and lighted the gas and went to work repairing the ravages made by generosity added to love. Which is always a tremendous task, dear friends— a mammoth task.

Within forty minutes her head was covered with tiny, close-lying curls that made her look wonderfully like a truant schoolboy. She looked at her reflection in the mirror long, carefully, and critically.

'If Jim doesn't kill me,' she said to herself, 'before he takes a second look at me, he'll say I look like a Coney Island chorus girl. But what could I do—oh! what could I do with a dollar and eighty-seven cents?'

At seven o'clock the coffee was made and the frying-pan was on the back of the stove, hot and ready to cook the chops.

Jim was never late. Della doubled the watch chain in her hand and sat on the corner of the table near the door that he always entered. Then she heard his step on the stair away down on the first flight, and she turned white for just a moment. She had a habit of saying little silent prayers about the simplest everyday things, and now she whispered: 'Please God, make him think I am still pretty.'

The door opened and Jim stepped in and closed it. He looked thin and very serious. Poor fellow, he was only twenty-two—and to be burdened with a family! He needed a new overcoat and he was without gloves.

Jim stepped inside the door, as immovable as a setter at the scent of quail. His eyes were fixed upon Della, and there was an expression in them that she could not read, and it terrified her. It was not anger, nor surprise, nor disapproval, nor horror, nor any of the sentiments that she had been prepared for. He simply stared at her fixedly with that peculiar expression on his face.

Della wriggled off the table and went for him.

'Jim, darling,' she cried, 'don't look at me that way. I had my hair cut off and sold it because I couldn't have lived through Christmas without giving you a present. It'll grow out again—you won't mind, will you? I just had to do it. My hair grows awfully fast. Say "Merry Christmas!" Jim, and let's be happy. You don't know what a nice—what a beautiful, nice gift I've got for you.'

'You've cut off your hair?' asked Jim, laboriously, as if he had not arrived at that patent fact yet even after the hardest mental labour.

'Cut it off and sold it,' said Della. 'Don't you like me just as well, anyhow? I'm me without my hair, ain't I?'

Jim looked about the room curiously.

'You say your hair is gone?' he said with an air almost of idiocy.

'You needn't look for it,' said Della. 'It's sold, I tell you—sold and gone, too. It's Christmas Eve, boy. Be good to me, for it went for you. Maybe the hairs of my head were numbered,' she went on with a sudden serious sweetness, 'but nobody could ever count my love for you. Shall I put the chops on, Jim?'

Out of his trance Jim seemed quickly to wake. He enfolded his Della. For ten seconds let us regard with discreet scrutiny some inconsequential object in the other direction. Eight dollars a week or a million a year—what is the difference? A mathematician or a wit would give you the wrong answer. The magi brought valuable gifts, but that was not among them. This dark assertion will be illuminated later on.

Jim drew a package from his overcoat pocket and threw it upon the table.

'Don't make any mistake, Dell,' he said, 'about me. I don't think there's anything in the way of a haircut or a shave or a shampoo that could make me like my girl any less. But if you'll unwrap that package you may see why you had me going awhile at first.'

White fingers and nimble tore at the string and paper. And then an ecstatic scream of joy; and then, alas! a quick feminine change to hysterical tears and wails, necessitating the immediate employment of all the comforting powers of the lord of the flat.

For there lay The Combs—the set of combs, side and back, that Della had worshipped for long in a Broadway window. Beautiful combs, pure tortoiseshell, with jewelled rims—just the shade to wear in the beautiful vanished hair. They were expensive combs, she knew, and her heart had simply craved and yearned over them without the least hope of possession. And now they were hers, but the tresses that should have adorned the coveted adornments were gone.

But she hugged them to her bosom, and at length she was able to look up with dim eyes and a smile and say: 'My hair grows so fast, Jim!'

And then Della leaped up like a little singed cat and cried, 'Oh, oh!'

Jim had not yet seen his beautiful present. She held it out to him eagerly upon her open palm. The dull precious metal seemed to flash with a reflection of her bright and ardent spirit.

'Isn't it a dandy, Jim? I hunted all over town to find it. You'll have to look at the time a hundred times a day now. Give me your watch. I want to see how it looks on it.'

Instead of obeying, Jim tumbled down on the couch and put his hands under the back of his head and smiled.

'Dell,' said he, 'let's put our Christmas presents away and keep 'em awhile. They're too nice to use just at present. I sold the watch to get the money to buy your combs. And now suppose you put the chops on.'

The magi, as you know, were wise men—wonderfully wise men—who brought gifts to the Babe in the manger. They invented the art of giving Christmas presents. Being wise, their gifts were no doubt wise ones, possibly bearing the privilege of exchange in case of duplication. And here I have lamely related to you the uneventful chronicle of two foolish children in a flat who most unwisely sacrificed for each other the greatest treasures of their house. But in a last word to the wise of these days, let it be said that of all who give gifts these two were the wisest. Of all who give and receive gifts, such as they are wisest. Everywhere they are wisest. They are the magi.

A Taste of Blood

Dillon woke with all his senses bruised and drugged, breathing heavily, unable to remember where he was.

The tortured impression that he had been lying unconscious on the bed for some long time, perhaps a day, changed harshly to raging pain. He was suddenly frightened by a ghastly conviction that his left arm had been severed just below the elbow and that the raw flesh was still hanging by a thread.

He sat up slowly. His head turned and throbbed like a ponderous roundabout. At times it seemed actually to click. Then it stopped momentarily and turned again, sickly. He shut his eyes, opened them glassily and slowly made several odd discoveries, the first of which was that he was still in his shirt and trousers. The second was that he had still one shoe on, the third that from top to bottom his left shirt sleeve was stiff as brown paper with thick dried blood.

He swung his feet slowly to the floor and sat for some minutes with his head buried in his hands. It wasn't as if he had been drunk the night before; he was somehow sure of that. It was more as if he had dragged up and down great slopes, among battering rocks. Every limb had a savage sprain in it; his head seemed to have been mercilessly banged by boulders.

Even when he at last stood up and looked at himself in the mirror hanging over the wash-stand he still found it utterly impossible to remember a fraction of anything that had happened to him. He hadn't the remotest idea of what day it was. He was unaware of the time of day; or how long he had been lying there with the arm oozing blood. His right cheek-bone had a sulphurous green bruise curled poisonously round it, oddly enough in the shape of a rough question mark. His thick black hair was matted with blood too. His left ear looked like a lump of red offal half-chewed by a dog.

In bitter pain he stripped off his shirt and made the further discovery that his arm was slit to the bone outside the crook of the elbow. It took him ten minutes or so to wash the arm free of blood and another ten minutes to wash the blood out of his hair and clean up the lacerated left ear. Sometimes he spat into the wash-basin. Clots of blood streaked from his mouth and the taste of blood was bitter too.

His ear, when washed, wasn't exactly painful. It merely burned like a dynamo. It caused him also to be deaf on his left side. As a result, when he walked about the room looking for a clean shirt and a jacket, he walked lop-sided, half off balance, like a drunk.

Dressed at last, he stood staring out of the window. His van, a small dark green one, stood slewed diagonally across the yard, the driving door still open. He couldn't remember anything about that either.

He went slowly downstairs. The back door was unlocked. Sunlight streamed across the yard. The metal of the van door was hot to the touch. He got the impression that the time was late afternoon.

Suddenly he was afflicted by a great thirst. He longed for a beer, a beer that would be endlessly deep and cold. He crawled into the van seat and then, after starting up the engine, discovered that he could scarcely crook his left arm.

He was forced to drive one-handed down the half-mile hill to the village. He was twenty-eight, a slow, mild rather awkward giant of a man, easy going, obliging, unquarrelsome, eager to please. He would do any kind of job for anybody at any time. In winter he cut chestnut poles. In spring he did hop-stringing. In summer there was cherry-picking and in September a month in the hop-gardens.

Hop-gardens? For a fraction of a second he remembered something about hop-gardens, then his mind was blank again. He stopped the van and sat staring down the street, trying to think. He was outside the *Black Horse* and the door was open. Then he knew it was after six o'clock.

He got out of the van and went up the stone steps of the *Black Horse* and into the bar. He hung on to the edge of the counter, half-faint with the exertion of climbing the steps. Joe Stevens was alone behind the bar, wiping glasses. The image of Joe swam about a bit but at least he knew it was Joe. That was something. He remembered Joe.

'Give me a beer, Joe, will you?'

Joe, shocked, staring hard, pulled the beer. A mass of froth overflowed yeastily across the brown counter. Dillon took the glass and held it to his lips. Suddenly he didn't want the beer. His thirst was violent as ever but underneath and behind it all his body felt white and frail with sickness. He set the glass back on the bar and said:

'Joe, where was I last night?'

'You wasn't in here.'

'No? Where was I?'

'You wasn't in here all night. What's happened to you? God Almighty, Dillon, what hit you?'

'I dunno. I can't remember. Where the hell was I?'

Joe stood mopping up the last of the froth from the bar.

'Last time I saw you was when you drove past here last night. Six o'clock that was. Dead on. I know because I was just opening up, just unbolting the door.'

'Six o'clock?'

'Yes. You had a girl in the front seat with you.'

'Girl?'

'Yes. I thought it was funny. I said to Edna "that's funny. Dillon with a girl. You don't often see Dillon with girls".'

'Girl? What girl?'

'Biggish girl. Fair. Wearing orange-coloured slacks. I didn't get a good look at her last night but I did this morning.'

'This morning?'

'She was in here this morning. About twelve o'clock. Asking for you. They told her up in the gardens she might find you here.'

'Up in the gardens? Is that where she was?'

'Started Monday she told me.'

'Monday? What's today?'

'Wednesday.'

Dillon took a slow drink of beer. His sickness receded a little. His body seemed less frail and white. He dwelt for half a minute on a blurred image of the hop-gardens, the figure of a girl slowly taking vague shape in it, cloudy and except for one detail unfamiliar.

'Wears a sort of band round her head? Blue, I think.'

'That's her,' Joe said. 'That's her.'

Dillon drove out of the village, back up the hill. The hop-gardens, a quarter stripped of vine, lay in three oblongs across the south slope of a valley. On the far side of the valley hills white with late barley lay crested by great summer-scorched woods, the upper edges of the trees already burnt to ginger, giving them the look of old, moulting bear skins.

He was still wondering whether to drive the van into the gardens or leave it on the road and walk the last hundred yards or so when he saw the girl walking down the hill. She was wearing the same orange slacks and the same bright blue band round her hair. Her shirt was the same colour as the band and her feet were in yellowish-brown sandals.

As soon as she saw him stop the van she started running. She was big in every detail, without being massive or heavy. The strong smooth thighs reminded him of a mare's and her brown-blonde hair, thick and held down by the band, was like a mane.

'God, there you are. Where have you been all day? I've been looking for you everywhere.'

She snatched open the van door, got into the seat beside and took one wide shocked look at him.

'God, your face. Your face! Whatever happened to your face?'

'Dunno. Can't remember. Must have had a crash with the van.'

She gave a brief bitter laugh that shocked his mild and unaggressive nature almost as much as the first sight of his battered face had done.

'Van, my foot. They did it. It's just like Iris said. Somebody gave them the tip. Somebody phoned them.'

He groped through clouds of dark bewilderment. He said he didn't think he knew quite what she was on about. Iris? Who was Iris? Who were they?

'Iris is my girl-friend. We work in Stepney together. We came down here to get a breath of fresh air.'

'Who are they then?'

She looked quickly up and down the road.

'I don't think we'd better stop here talking. We'd better go somewhere else. Where you took me last night. Let's go there.'

'Where was that?'

'Don't you remember? Up on the hills there. You don't remember? There was a big wood and we pulled inside. There was a hedge with honeysuckle on it. I didn't know what it was and you picked a bit for me. You don't remember?'

He said he didn't remember. Not only that part but all the other parts. Not a thing. It was all a blank. He'd had a job even to remember her.

'Let's go,' she said. 'It'll be quieter there.' A big scarlet petrol tanker drove past, setting up a great wash of air that started all the skeins of hops swaying across the gardens like pale green curtains. 'No. I don't think we'd better. Can you think of somewhere else? Somewhere quiet and out of sight? Off the road?'

He sat staring at the dashboard, his left hand on the ignition key, trying hard to do his first real coherent piece of thinking of the day. After almost half a minute a gap opened in the deep clouds of his confusion and he said:

'Up in the old sand quarry. That ought to do. Nobody ever goes up there.'

'That sounds all right. Let's go up there.'

He paused for a few seconds longer before attempting to turn the ignition key.

'We could go back to my place. You must be hungry. We could get you something to eat.'

'I'm not hungry,' she said. 'I'd rather be out in the fresh air anyway. I feel freer outside. Besides, they know where you live by now. It wouldn't be any good going there.'

She gave him a look of sudden tenderness, urging him to get started, at the same time giving his left arm a sudden squeeze of affection. In agony he let out a gasp of pain and at last, sick to the core of himself, turned the key.

'Now see if you can't remember. What did you do when you left me last night? Outside the hop-gardens.'

He sat in the car, staring across the old deserted sand quarry. It formed a sort of arena, a hundred and fifty yards across, its walls rising thirty or forty feet in a rough circle like cliffs of rough, amber-coloured cheese. A shaggy fringe of burnt grass grew from the top and here and there big stumpy elderberry trees had taken root in gaps among the stone. The floor of it was like some arid bone-yard, completely flat and white, from which a flood had swept the bones away. From scores of holes in the cliffs dark clouds of sand-martins poured and swooped, crying thinly.

'You kissed me good-night and then went down the hill. It must have been half past ten. Perhaps eleven.'

'Kissed you good-night?'

She gave a short laugh and quickly brushed her lips across his own.

'Yes. Kissed. Like that, only better. You don't even remember that, do you?'

He had once again to confess that he didn't remember.

'Do you remember anything about being followed by a motor-bike? Perhaps two motor-bikes? Perhaps three? Does that mean anything to you?'

No: that didn't mean anything to him either.

'Tell me,' he said, 'who they are.'

'I'm not sure how many there were yet,' she said. 'Three at least. Perhaps five. So I wouldn't know who they were. But I know one for sure.'

'Yes?'

'He's a fellow named Tooley.' She made a movement as if to hold his arm and then remembered the pain of the previous time. 'I may as well tell you. I was friends with him. Then he started to get big. Big-headed. Big-mouthed. Swelled-headed. The lot. Then he swizzed my brother out of seventy quid on a motor-bike deal. Then went about boasting of it, shooting his fat mouth. He's as mad as a monkey about motor-bikes. They all are.'

The talk of motor-bikes entered Dillon's mind with the sudden click of a key. It seemed, he thought, that he might be on the verge of remembering things.

'So we had one big hell of a stack-up. I told him I'd never see him again and I damn well meant it too. He started to rough me up then—that's all he knows about, roughing people up—but I hammered him back again. He knows I'm not scared of him. You don't have to be if you get on that flaming bike with him. I know.'

Dillon sat thinking again of motor-bikes. A raw note of fast engines searing up a hill scorched the vague distances of his memory. Across the quarry a huge segment of shadow lay almost black against the brilliant face of sand.

'Got a cigarette?' she said suddenly. 'I don't smoke much since this cancer scare. But I could do with one now.'

He fumbled in his pockets. He brought out half a packet of cigarettes and a lighter. He sprang the lighter catch and it flamed the first time.

'Thanks,' she said and blew smoke.

'You'd better hold on to the lighter,' Dillon said. 'You might want it again.'

'Just thought of something,' she said. She slipped the lighter from one hand to the other and back again. 'Bet you don't remember my name.'

'I thought it was Shirley.'

She laughed. It was a friendly, deep sound.

'First thing you asked me. Said you liked it. Thought it suited me. Olga, not Shirley.'

'You must think I'm a damn fool.'

'You looked at me all afternoon,' she said. 'I could feel you out of the back of my head. I can see you now. You were riding on the back of that trailer and every time you went by I had a funny sort of feeling you wanted me. You remember all that, surely, or don't you?'

All of a sudden he saw her again as he had seen her all the golden afternoon in the hop-garden, his memory absolutely bright. He could see her big sun-reddened arms pulling at the bine. She was looking at him with large bee-brown eyes and the orange slacks were stretched tight across her thighs.

'I remember now,' Dillon said. 'It's all starting to come back.'

'Remember anything else?' she said. 'About last night, I mean?'

In an almost explosive flash that too came back. The searing roar of motor-bike engines dinned itself cruelly into his consciousness. He was driving home in darkness down the hill. A bike suddenly came up at great speed beside him, cutting so fast across his head-lights that he braked and swerved. Then it stuck in front of him, full in his head-lights, never more than five or six yards away. Then a second bike came roaring up beside him and he could hear a third at his back.

He saw the faces of the first two riders grinning with wide leers under their black crash helmets. He remembered yelling madly, shaking his fist out of the window. Every now and then he accelerated too. They had him trapped in a sort of mobile vice. There was no escaping. And finally when he stopped they too stopped. They had him caught as if he were a criminal on the run and the first thing he saw on getting out of the driving seat was the swing of a big spanner in the lights of the van.

Slowly he told her all this. She listened without a word. He was still distraught and bewildered by the naked recollection of the first spanner blow crashing against his ear and all he could ask was:

'Who'd want to do a thing like that to me? What have I done? I was just going home. Minding my own business.'

She threw her cigarette out of the window. She played tensely with the lighter, tipping it from hand to hand.

'Somebody must have told them. Like I said, somebody must have phoned.' She suddenly let out a half-shout. Her voice was savage. 'Iris. Nobody could have done it only Iris. My friend, the jealous bitch, my friend. God, what a blasted fool I've been. What a blasted, cock-eyed fool.'

She rammed a second cigarette into her mouth. She struck the lighter into flame and then lit the cigarette, her fingers shaking with anger.

'We'd better go,' she said. 'I got to have a few words with Iris. I got things to say to that bitch. My friend.'

Dillon supposed they must have travelled less than half a mile from the sand quarry when her ears, far sharper than his, suddenly picked up the sound of bike engines from some distance behind. A second after she heard it she shouted:

'Turn off: It mightn't be them but turn off all the same. Is there some other way back to the quarry? We'd be out of sight there.'

'Think so. I'll take the next turn.'

Dillon drove faster, half skidding round the next turn. In another two minutes a thick chestnut copse cut off all sight of the road behind. From under the dark chestnut leaves the wind blew cool into the windows of the car, but he could feel sweat pouring down his face, stinging the smashed raw flesh of his ear.

Suddenly she picked up the sound of bikes again, roaring past the turn.

'Five of them this time. Two big Nortons in front. I'd know them anywhere.'

Dillon stepped hard on the accelerator pedal. In the confusion he was having some difficulty in remembering the road. Beyond the chestnut copses was a field of late wheat, half-cut, a big red combine harvester standing in its centre, and beyond that a farm.

Suddenly he remembered a back-cut, not much more than a cart-track, behind the farm. He slowed down and swerved into it and in another five minutes he could see once again the rough, amber-coloured cliffs of sand.

He stopped the car and switched off the engine. His face was running with a heavy sweat of weakness. He had an overwhelming desire to get out of the car and walk about and drink fresh air but he suddenly knew his legs would never carry him.

She suddenly recognized the fresh agony of his weakness and drew down his head and let it rest on her shoulder. She got a handkerchief and wiped some of his sweat away. Once her thick hair fell across his face and the act of its falling drew a curtain across his memory, so that for a second time he didn't know where he was.

He was shaken out of this half-coma by her sitting up with a violent jerk. She could hear the bikes again, she said, and this time her voice was a whisper.

'Where?'

'I can hear them coming up the hill. They're going back now they couldn't find you.'

He saw her with vague eyes. She was tense, her face taut with the strain of listening. Soon the sound of engines was so loud that he could even hear it himself. The bikes, it seemed to him, roared across the mouth of the quarry. The walled arena was battered with echoes.

Then it was suddenly quiet: oddly and unhealthily quiet, like the quiet after sudden thunder.

'They've gone,' he said, his mind still too vague to notice that she didn't answer.

Through sheer weakness his head dropped again on her shoulder. This time she made no attempt to touch it. She sat upright, braced as if to receive a blow. Then suddenly she half leapt to the window, leaning out.

'Oh! my God. Like I thought,' she said.

'What is it? What's up?'

'They're here. Five of them. Over there.'

A single bike started to come at slow and sinister speed across the sand. The remaining four lined up behind, engines ticking over, closing the gap in the quarry.

The bike came up to the van and stopped. The figure riding it was a big, crusty fellow with a square jaw. His crash helmet was black. His leather driving coat was black too. A skull and cross-bones was painted in white across the back of it. He seemed about nineteen.

'Well, if it ain't our Olga. Well, well. Long time no see.'

'Buzz off. Make yourself scarce.'

'I only just got here. How's the boy friend? Looks nice and healthy to me.'

'How'd you know we were here?'

'Funny, really. Little accident of nature. You know. We thought it looked like a good place to water the horses.'

'Buzz off. Go on, buzz. Get lost. Before I lose my temper.'

'Now, now. If you don't mind your manners, little lady, I might mark you.'

She played with the lighter. She clenched it in her right fist in such a way that the nozzle protruded through the two centre knuckles.

'And there might be ways of marking you too, big-head. Now buzz. Start motoring.'

'Billy Boy looks bone-lazy to me. Boy friend looks tired. I thought you like strong blokes? Country boy needs exercise. Start driving, country boy.'

'Driving?' Dillon said. 'Where?'

'Just round. Just round and round and round and round. Till me and the boys tell you to stop. Won't be long. Couple of hours or so. I've got time.'

Dillon, almost too weak to hold the wheel, hesitated.

'Better drive,' she said. 'This one's the big strong man. He loves odds. Five to one. He loves that. Tell me something. Did Iris phone you? Was it that jealous bitch?'

'Iris?' he said. 'Who's Iris? Never heard of her. Drive.'

Dillon started to drive. Only two bikes now guarded the entrance to the quarry. Like evil black beetles, the other three took up the escort of the van, one on each flank, the other three or four yards ahead. Now and then the three black helmeted riders signalled Dillon to go faster. On the cramped circle of the quarry floor they hotted the speed up to thirty, then forty and beyond. To Dillon it seemed like fifty. He drove as in a drunken daze, his head battered by engine roar, his vision bewildered by the wild flight of frightened martins crying everywhere.

After the fifth or sixth circuit they thought up a trick. Each time the van turned westward the slanting sun drove shafts of light flat into Dillon's eyes, dazzling him. Half-blind, he struggled desperately to keep the van upright. He drove as into a blazing arc-light, each rider in turn jinking in front of him, swerving, half-horizontal, like a dirt-track rider, dragging feet, raising searing white dust against his screen.

He now began to drive in a sheer suspense of terror. He lost all count of the number of circuits. Only half-conscious, he presently felt himself to be performing in a wall of death, in a dusty nightmare, on some hellish fairground. In his terrified concentration on the blinding dust in front of him he was no longer even aware of the girl.

It must have been at the twentieth circuit or so that his head seemed half to fall from his shoulders and the entire face of the quarry turned black. The girl shouted and grabbed the wheel. A second later a jinking rider sliced in front of her and she drove straight at him, the engine stalling violently as she cut him down.

In a flash she was out of the van, the cigarette lighter in her hand, already alight. Tooley lay half pinned under the big Norton, petrol pouring from the carburettor.

She stood two yards from him, holding the lighter at arm's length.

'Now will you buzz? or shall I put it to the carburettor?'

'Don't be a bloody fool! Take it away! I don't want to burn!'

'Then call them off from me!' The other two riders were beetling madly up from behind the van. 'Call them off, I tell you, or I'll throw it. I don't mind burning. I'll burn. I'm not scared of that. Call them off, I tell you!'

She raised the lighter high above her head as if to throw it. Tooley actually screamed, yelling for the bike to be lifted off from him.

'That's right,' she said. 'Lift his cradle. Take him away in his cradle now.'

The other two riders pulled the bike from Tooley, who swung fiercely back into the saddle, white and savage.

'I've a good mind to run you down for that, lady.'

She held the lighter out to him, like a torch.

'Yes?' she said. 'Try.'

Ten seconds later a slow procession of three bikes started across the sand. It joined the other two at the gap and went on like a dusty cortège to the road.

The girl went back to the van and sat with Dillon. The sun began to go down. Without a word she drew his head on to her shoulder and kissed his face. For a long time he had neither the strength nor the will to say a word either but finally he moved and brushed his mouth against her own.

'It'll soon be dark,' she said. 'Think you can drive?'

'Think so.'

'Take it steady,' she said. 'Take it easy. You think there might be time to gather me a piece of honeysuckle? It might do something to sweeten the air.'

Dillon leaned his head out of the window, breathing hard.

'It feels sweet to me already,' he said.

He started the engine. With pain he drove slowly forward and once again the air was filled with a crying tumult of wings.

Ernest Hemingway

The End of Something

In the old days Hortons Bay was a lumbering town. No one who
lived in it was out of sound of the big saws in the mill by the lake.
Then one year there were no more logs to make lumber. The
lumber schooners came into the bay and were loaded with the cut
of the mill that stood stacked in the yard. All the piles of lumber
were carried away. The big mill building had all its machinery
that was removable taken out and hoisted on board one of the
schooners by the men who had worked in the mill. The schooner
moved out of the bay toward the open lake carrying the two great
saws, the travelling carriage that hurled the logs against the revolv-
ing, circular saws, and all the rollers, wheels, belts and iron piled
on a hull-deep load of lumber. Its open hold covered with canvas
and lashed tight, the sails of the schooner filled and it moved out
into the open lake, carrying with it everything that had made the
mill a mill and Hortons Bay a town.

The one-storey bunk houses, the eating-house, the company store,
the mill offices, and the big mill itself stood deserted in the acres of
sawdust that covered the swampy meadow by the shore of the bay.

Ten years later there was nothing of the mill left except the
broken white limestone of its foundations showing through the
swampy second growth as Nick and Marjorie rowed along the
shore. They were trolling along the edge of the channel bank where
the bottom dropped off suddenly from sandy shallows to twelve
feet of dark water. They were trolling on their way to the point
to set night lines for rainbow trout.

'There's our old ruin, Nick,' Marjorie said.

Nick, rowing, looked at the white stone in the green trees.

'There it is,' he said.

'Can you remember when it was a mill?' Marjorie asked.

'I can just remember,' Nick said.

'It seems more like a castle,' Marjorie said.

Nick said nothing. They rowed on out of sight of the mill, following the shore line. Then Nick cut across the bay.

'They aren't striking,' he said.

'No,' Marjorie said. She was intent on the rod all the time they trolled, even when she talked. She loved to fish. She loved to fish with Nick.

Close beside the boat a big trout broke the surface of the water. Nick pulled hard on one oar so the boat would turn and the bait spinning far behind would pass where the trout was feeding. As the trout's back came up out of the water the minnows jumped wildly. They sprinkled the surface like a handful of shot thrown into the water. Another trout broke water, feeding on the other side of the boat.

'They're feeding,' Marjorie said.

'But they won't strike,' Nick said.

He rowed the boat around to troll past both the feeding fish, then headed it for the point. Marjorie did not reel in until the boat touched the shore.

They pulled the boat up the beach and Nick lifted out a pail of live perch. The perch swam in the water in the pail. Nick caught three of them with his hands and cut their heads off and skinned them while Marjorie chased with her hands in the bucket, finally caught a perch, cut its head off and skinned it. Nick looked at her fish.

'You don't want to take the ventral fin out,' he said. 'It'll be all right for bait but it's better with the ventral fin in.'

He hooked each of the skinned perch through the tail. There were two hooks attached to a leader on each rod. Then Marjorie rowed the boat out over the channel-bank, holding the line in her teeth, and looking toward Nick, who stood on the shore holding the rod and letting the line run out from the reel.

'That's about right,' he called.

'Should I let it drop?' Marjorie called back, holding the line in her hand.

'Sure. Let it go.' Marjorie dropped the line overboard and watched the baits go down through the water.

She came in with the boat and ran the second line out the same way. Each time Nick set a heavy slab of driftwood across the butt of the rod to hold it solid and propped it up at an angle with a small slab. He reeled in the slack line so the line ran taut out to where the bait rested on the sandy floor of the channel and set the click on the reel. When a trout, feeding on the bottom, took the bait it would run with it, taking line out of the reel in a rush and making the reel sing with the click on.

Marjorie rowed up the point a little way so she would not disturb the line. She pulled hard on the oars and the boat went way up the beach. Little waves came in with it. Marjorie stepped out of the boat and Nick pulled the boat high up the beach.

'What's the matter, Nick?' Marjorie asked.

'I don't know,' Nick said, getting wood for a fire.

They made a fire with driftwood. Marjorie went to the boat and brought a blanket. The evening breeze blew the smoke toward the point, so Marjorie spread the blanket out between the fire and the lake.

Marjorie sat on the blanket with her back to the fire and waited for Nick. He came over and sat down beside her on the blanket. In back of them was the close second-growth timber of the point and in front was the bay with the mouth of Hortons Creek. It was not quite dark. The fire-light went as far as the water. They could both see the two steel rods at an angle over the dark water. The fire glinted on the reels.

Marjorie unpacked the basket of supper.

'I don't feel like eating,' said Nick.

'Come on and eat, Nick.'

'All right.'

They ate without talking, and watched the two rods and the fire-light in the water.

'There's going to be a moon to-night,' said Nick. He looked across the bay to the hills that were beginning to sharpen against the sky. Beyond the hills he knew the moon was coming up.

'I know it,' Marjorie said happily.

'You know everything,' Nick said.

'Oh, Nick, please cut it out! Please, please don't be that way!'

'I can't help it,' Nick said. 'You do. You know everything. That's the trouble. You know you do.'

Marjorie did not say anything.

'I've taught you everything. You know you do. What don't you know, anyway?'

'Oh, shut up,' Marjorie said. 'There comes the moon.'

They sat on the blanket without touching each other and watched the moon rise.

'You don't have to talk silly,' Marjorie said. 'What's really the matter?'

'I don't know.'

'Of course you know.'

'No, I don't.'

'Go on and say it.'

Nick looked on at the moon, coming up over the hills.

'It isn't fun any more.'

He was afraid to look at Marjorie. Then he looked at her. She sat there with her back toward him. He looked at her back. 'It isn't fun any more. Not any of it.'

She didn't say anything. He went on. 'I feel as though everything was gone to hell inside of me. I don't know, Marge. I don't know what to say.'

He looked on at her back.

'Isn't love any fun?' Marjorie said.

'No,' Nick said. Marjorie stood up. Nick sat there, his head in his hands.

'I'm going to take the boat,' Marjorie called to him. 'You can walk back around the point.'

'All right,' Nick said. 'I'll push the boat off for you.'

'You don't need to,' she said. She was afloat in the boat on the water with the moonlight on it. Nick went back and lay down with his face in the blanket by the fire. He could hear Marjorie rowing on the water.

He lay there for a long time. He lay there while he heard Bill come into the clearing walking around through the woods. He felt Bill coming up to the fire. Bill didn't touch him, either.

'Did she go all right?' Bill said.

'Yes,' Nick said, lying, his face on the blanket.

'Have a scene?'

'No, there wasn't any scene.'

'How do you feel?'

'Oh, go away, Bill! Go away for a while.'

Bill selected a sandwich from the lunch basket and walked over to have a look at the rods.

Frank O'Connor

The Impossible Marriage

It wasn't till he was nearly thirty that Jim Grahame realized the trick that life had played on him. Up to that time he had lived very much like any other young man, with no great notion that he was being imposed upon. His father had died ten years before. Jim, an accountant in a provision store, had continued to accept his father's responsibilities, and his mother, a lively, sweet-natured little woman, had kept house for him in the way that only mothers can. They lived on in the house into which she had married; a big, roomy, awkward house on the edge of the country where the rent they paid was barely enough to keep the building in repair. Jim had never been very shy with girls, but none of them he had met seemed to him to be half the woman his mother was, and, unknown to himself, he was turning into a typical comfortable old bachelor who might or might not at the age of forty-five decide to establish a family of his own. His mother spoiled him, of course, and, in the way of only children, he had a troubled conscience because of the way he took advantage of it. But spoiling is a burden that the majority of men can carry a great deal of without undue hardship.

Then, by the seaside in Crosshaven, one Sunday, he went for a walk with a girl called Eileen Clery, who lived in the same quarter of Cork as himself, though he had never noticed her before. She wasn't the sort of girl who thrusts herself on people's attention, though she was good-looking enough, with a thin face that lit up beautifully when she smiled, and pale hair with gold lights in it. He tried to flirt with her, and was surprised and a little offended by her quick, almost violent, withdrawal. He had not mistaken her for a flighty type, but neither had he expected to meet an untouchable.

The curious thing was that she seemed to like him, and even arranged to meet him again. This time they sat in a nook on the cliffs, and Jim became more pressing. To his astonishment, she began to cry. He was exasperated, but he pretended a solicitude he did not altogether feel, and when she saw him apparently distressed, she sat up and smiled, though her tears still continued to flow freely. 'It's not that I wouldn't like it, Jim,' she said, drying her eyes and blowing her nose into a ridiculous little scrap of a handkerchief, 'only I don't like thinking about it.'

'Why on earth not, Eileen?' he asked with some amusement.

'Well, you see, I'm an only child, and I have my mother to look after,' she said, still sniffing.

'And I'm an only child, and I have a mother to look after,' Jim replied triumphantly, and then laughed outright at the absurdity of the coincidence. 'We're a pair,' he added with a rueful chuckle.

'Yes, aren't we?' Eileen said, laughing and sobbing at once, and then she rested her head on his chest, and made no further difficulties about his love-making.

Now, all books on the subject describe attraction in similar terms; tanned chests and voluptuous contours which really have very little to do with the matter. But what they rarely mention, the most powerful of all, is human loneliness. This is something that women face earlier than men, and Eileen had already faced it. Jim, though he had not faced it in the same way, was perceptive enough to see it reaching out before him, and up there on the cliffs overlooking Cork Harbour, watching a score of little sailing boats headed for Currabinny, they realized that they were in love, and all the more in love because their position was so obviously hopeless.

After that, they met regularly every week in Cork, to walk, or go to the pictures when it rained. They did it in the way of only children, taking precautions that became something of a joke to those who knew them. One evening, a girl crossing the New Bridge saw Jim Grahame standing there, and when she came to the second bridge was amused to see Eileen. 'Excuse my interfering, Miss Clery,' she said, 'but if it's Mr Grahame you're waiting for, he's waiting for you at the other bridge.' Eileen didn't know where to look; she blushed, she laughed, and finally joined her hands and said, 'Oh, thank you, thank you,' and ran like the wind.

It was like them to meet that way, miles from home, because they were pursued by the sense of guilt. They felt more pity for their mothers than for themselves and did their best to hide their dreadful secret out of some instinctive understanding of the fear of loneliness and old age that besets women whose families have grown and whose husbands are dead. Perhaps they even understood it too well, and apprehended more of it than was really there.

Mrs Grahame, whose intelligence service was better than Mrs Clery's, was the first to speak of the matter to them.

'I hear you're great friends with a girl called Clery from the Cross,' she said one evening in a tone of modest complaint. Jim was shaving by the back door. He started and turned to her with a look of amusement, but she was absorbed in her knitting, as always when she did not wish to look him in the face.

'Go on!' he said. 'Who told you that?'

'Why wouldn't I hear it when the whole road knows it?' she replied, avoiding his question. She liked her little mysteries. 'Wouldn't you bring her up some night?'

'You wouldn't mind?'

'Why would I mind, child? Little enough company we see.'

This was another of her favourite myths; that she never saw or spoke to anyone, though Jim could do little or nothing that she didn't hear about sooner or later.

One evening he brought Eileen home for tea, and though she was nervous and giggly, he could see that his mother took to her at once. Mrs Grahame worshipped her son, but she had always wished for a daughter, someone she could talk to as she could not talk to a man. Later in the evening, Eileen, realizing that she really was welcome, began to relax, and she and his mother exchanged the sort of gossip they both loved.

'Ah, Dinny Murphy was a bad head to her,' his mother would say darkly, referring to some object of charity in the neighbourhood.

'No, no, no, Mrs Grahame,' Eileen would say hastily, in her eagerness laying her hand on Mrs Grahame's arm. 'Poor Dinny wasn't the worst.'

'Look at that now!' Mrs Grahame would cry, putting down her knitting to fix Eileen with eyes that were bleak with tragedy. 'And the things they said about him! Eileen, haven't people *bad* tongues?'

'No, he wasn't, he wasn't,' Eileen would repeat, shaking her head. 'He took a drop, of course, but which of them doesn't, would you tell me?'

And Jim, who said nothing, smiled as he noticed how the voice of Eileen, young, eager, and intelligent, blended with his mother's in a perfect harmony of gossip. Mrs Grahame did not let her go without hinting delicately at her lost and lonely condition that made it impossible for her to know the truth about anything, and made her promise to come again. She became accustomed to Eileen's visits, and was quite hurt if a week went by without one. She even said with great resignation that of course she was no company for a lively young girl like that.

Then it was Mrs Clery's turn. She might hear of Eileen's visit to the Grahames, and be upset, but, on the other hand, she might be equally upset by an unexpected visit. So Eileen had to prepare her by telling her first how Jim was situated with regard to his own mother so that she wouldn't think he came to the house with any designs on Eileen. All they had to live on was Eileen's earnings and a few shillings pension which her mother drew.

They lived in a tiny cottage in a terrace off the road, with a parlour, a kitchen that they used as a living room, and two attic bedrooms upstairs. Mrs Clery was a shrewd old lady with a battered humorous face. She suffered from a variety of ailments, and, being slightly deaf, complained of them at great length in a loud, hectoring tone. She would put a firm hand on her interlocutor's knee while she talked, to make sure he didn't escape, and then stare blankly at the fireplace in concentration.

'So then, Jim, I had this second pain I was telling you about, and I had Dr O'Mahoney to the house, and he said—what did Dr O'Mahoney say about the second pain, Eileen?'

'He said you were an old humbug,' bawled Eileen.

'Dr O'Mahoney?' her mother said in wonderment. 'He did not. Ah, you divil you!'

At home, Eileen talked nervously, at the top of her voice, interrupting, contradicting, and bantering her mother till the old woman's face wrinkled up with glee and she blinked at Jim and groaned: 'Didn't I say she was a divil, Jim? Did you ever hear a girl talk to her mother that way? I'll engage you don't talk like that to your own poor mother.'

'His mother isn't always grousing,' Eileen yelled blithely from the backyard.

'Grousing? Who's grousing?' asked Mrs Clery, her eyes half closing with pleasure, like a cat's when you stroke it. 'Oh, my, I live in terror of her, Jim, boy, you never heard such a tongue! And the lies she tells! Me grousing!'

All the same it was pleasant for Jim and Eileen to have a place to turn to on a wet night when they didn't want to go to the pictures. Mostly, they went to Jim's. Mrs Grahame was more jealous than Eileen's mother. Even a hint of slight on the part of either of them would reduce her to mutinous tears, but if they sat with her for half an hour, she would get up and tiptoe gently out of the room as though she thought they were asleep. Her jealousy was only the measure of her generosity.

'Wisha, Jim,' she said roguishly one evening, putting down her knitting, 'wouldn't you and Eileen make a match of it?'

'A match?' Jim repeated mockingly, looking up from his book. 'I suppose you want to get rid of me?'

His mother could usually be diverted from any subject by teasing because she took everything literally even if she rarely took it far.

'Indeed, what a thing I'd do!' she said in a huff and went on with her knitting, full of childish rage at his reception of her generous proposal. But, of course, it didn't last. Ten minutes later, having forgotten her huff, she added, this time as though speaking to herself: 'Why, then, you wouldn't find many like her.'

'And where would we live?' he asked with gentle irony.

'My goodness, haven't ye the house?' she said, looking at him severely over her glasses. 'You don't think I'd stop to be in your way?'

'Oh, so you'd go to the workhouse and let Mrs Clery come here?'

'Wisha, aren't things very peculiar?' she said vaguely, and he knew that she was brooding on the coincidence by which he and Eileen had been drawn together. His mother and he were both familiar with the situation in its simple form, common as it is in Ireland, and could have listed a score of families where a young man or woman 'walked out' for years before he or she was in a position to marry, too often only to find themselves too old or tired for it.

'We're not thinking in that direction at all, Mrs Grahame, thank you all the same,' he said, giving her a sweet smile. 'It's got to be a double murder or nothing at all.'

He knew that in spite of her jealousy, Mrs Grahame resented this fate for them, but Mrs Clery jovially pretended that they should be grateful for their good fortune.

'Ye don't know how well off ye are,' she said. 'Ye're young and healthy; a lot ye have to complain of. The way they rush into marriage you'd think they were robbing a bank. Soon enough they get tired of it, and then, oh, my! nothing is bad enough for them to say about one another.'

'So you don't approve of marriage, Mammy?' Eileen would ask demurely.

'Who said I don't approve of marriage?' her mother asked suspiciously, certain that the 'divils' were trapping her again. 'What matter whether you approve of it or not? That doesn't make it any better. Let ye be young while ye can, Jim,' she counselled, laying a rocky hand on Jim's knee. 'Ye'll be married long enough.'

But, of course, Eileen and himself did not share her views. On their evening walks they usually passed through one of the new developments, glanced into half-built houses with the enthusiasm of the children who played Cowboys and Indians in them; chatted with young husbands digging in little patches of garden that were mainly builders' rubble, and let themselves be invited in for cups of tea by young couples in all the pride and joy of recent possession. They saw nothing of the ugliness of it. They saw only the newness of everything as though it were life itself renewed; the way the evening sunlight brought up the freshness of the paint, the whiteness of the curtains, the tender green of the new grass. Later in the evening Eileen would say, shaking her head: 'I didn't think the curtains were right in the big corner windows, Jim, did you?' and Jim would know she had furnished the house in her own mind.

That year Jim suggested that he and Eileen should take their holidays together. This didn't suit Mrs Clery at all. She was sure it would give Eileen a bad name. Mrs Clery was all for their being young while they could, but only as long as they were being young under her eye. Jim knew it wasn't Eileen's good name that her mother worried about at all, but the possibility that their holiday might start something she could not control. He had his way; they went to a seaside place north of Dublin, and walked and swam and sunbathed to their hearts' content for a fortnight, going into the city when it rained.

On their way home, looking out at the Galtee mountains from the window of their carriage, he said: 'Next time we go on holidays like that, we should be married. It's not the same thing.'

'No, Jim, it isn't,' she agreed. 'But what can we do?'

'What's to stop us getting married?' he asked with a smile.

'Now?' she asked in alarm. 'But what would we do with our mothers?'

'What we do with them now,' he said with a shrug.

'You mean get married and go on the way we're going?'

'Why not? Of course, it's not what we want, but it's better than nothing.'

'But suppose—well, Jim, you know yourself there might be children.'

'I should hope so,' he replied. 'We can cross that bridge when we come to it. But anyhow, there's no particular reason we should have kids yet.'

'But Jim,' she asked timidly, 'wouldn't people talk?'

'Do you think they don't talk now?'

Jim was like that, and what Jim thought his mother would think, regardless of public opinion. She, of course, had seen nothing wrong with their going on holidays together, and Eileen, who had felt rather doubtful of it herself, now knew that she was right. She felt he was probably right now too, but she wasn't sure.

The more she thought of it, the more she felt he was, though her reasons were of a different kind. Jim didn't want to wait; he didn't want to grow old and sour in expectation of the day when they could get married; he wanted something, however little it might be, of the pleasure of marriage while they were still young enough to enjoy it. Eileen thought of it in a more mystical way as a sort of betrothal which would bind them to one another, whatever life might have in store for them. She knew it was too much to hope that she and Jim would both be set free at the same time; one would be bound to be free long before the other, and then the real temptation would begin.

But she knew that even this she would not get without a fight with her mother. Mrs Clery was conventional to the heart, and besides she knew what happened in marriage. Eileen was very sweet and gentle now, but Eileen as wife or mother would be an altogether different proposition and one an old lady might be unable to handle at all.

'What a thing you'd do!' Mrs Clery gasped with one hand on her hip. 'What sort of marriage would that be? Him living there and you living here! You'd have the whole town laughing at you.'

'I don't really see what they'd have to laugh at, Mammy,' Eileen said earnestly. 'Any more than they have now.'

'Go off with him!' her mother said brokenly. 'Go off with him! I'd sooner go to the workhouse than be disgraced by ye.'

'But, Mammy,' persisted Eileen, laughing in spite of herself, 'we won't do anything to disgrace you, and you won't have to go to the workhouse or anywhere else.'

Mrs Grahame was upset too, but it was her pride that was hurt.

What the neighbours would say did not worry her at all, but it seemed to her that it was her dependence on Jim that forced him into this caricature of a marriage. If by getting out of his way she could have made it easier for him, she would cheerfully have gone into the workhouse. But when Jim explained that even if he agreed to her doing so, it would change nothing regarding Eileen and her mother, she saw that he was right. When next Eileen called, Mrs Grahame embraced her and muttered: 'Ye poor children! Ye poor, distracted children!'

'You don't think we're doing wrong, Mrs Grahame?' Eileen asked, beginning to be tearful herself.

'Sure, how could you be doing wrong, child?' Mrs Grahame exclaimed angrily. 'Why would ye care what anybody thinks? People who never sacrificed a thing in their lives!'

Then Mrs Clery threw a fit of sulks, would not speak to Jim when he called, and finally refused to attend what she called 'the mock wedding'. Mrs Clery had little experience of that sort of thing, but she did know when she had been tricked, and she had been tricked by Jim. He had come to the house as a friend and stolen her only daughter from under her eyes. As for all this talk of putting her first, she didn't believe a word of it. A man who would do what he had done would think nothing of putting arsenic in her cup of tea.

Before she left for the church that morning, Eileen went in to her mother and asked gently: 'Mammy, won't you even wish me luck?' But all her mother said was 'Go away, you bold thing!'

'I'll be back tomorrow night in time to get your supper, Mammy,' Eileen said meekly.

'You needn't come back at all,' said her mother.

Eileen was very upset, but Mrs Grahame only scoffed at it when they said goodbye outside the church.

'Ah, she'll get over it, child,' she said. 'Old people are all lick alike. I'm the same myself, if the truth was known. I'll see her on the way home and give her a bit of my mind.'

'And, Mrs Grahame, if you wouldn't mind making her an egg flip, she'd be easier to talk to,' Eileen said earnestly. 'She's very fond of egg flips, and she likes a lot of whiskey in them.'

'I'll give her an egg flip,' said Mrs Grahame, suddenly light-hearted because her own savage jealousy melted in the thought of comforting another old woman in her tantrums. She had a job on her hands, even with the egg flip.

'Don't talk to me, ma'am!' cried Mrs Clery. 'Young people today are all the same; all selfish, all for pleasure.'

'How can you say it, Mrs Clery?' Mrs Grahame asked indignantly. 'There isn't a better daughter in Ireland. I'd be the last to criticize Jim, but I only wish I had one like her.'

'And when the children start coming?' asked Mrs Clery, looking at her as if she were out of her mind.

'You reared one yourself.'

' 'Tisn't alike, ma'am,' said Mrs Clery and refused to be comforted. She was intelligent enough to realize that the presence of another baby in the house might rob her of some of the attention to which she felt entitled, and might even result in her being totally deprived of her privileges. Young people today were so selfish!

After their one-day honeymoon, Jim and Eileen obediently returned to their duties as though they had never been married at all. Yet Eileen, when you met her on the road, was exceedingly lighthearted and lightheaded, sporting her ring like any young bride. She needed all the joy her new position gave her because her mother had been shrewd enough in her summing up of what the neighbours' attitude would be. The marriage had become a matter of scandalous jokes, and remained so as long as it lasted. Even from intimate friends, Eileen got little jabs that reminded her of her anomalous wifehood. It wasn't that the neighbours were uncharitable, but their feelings about marriage, like their feelings about death, had a certain fierceness that was obvious even in their dislike of second marriages. This marriage that seemed to end at the church door was a mockery of all they believed in, so they took their revenge as people will whose dearest beliefs have been slighted.

Jim affected not to notice the scandal. He had his mother's curious imperviousness to public opinion, and he dropped in on Eileen as though nothing in particular could be said against him. Eileen dropped in rather more frequently on him and his mother, and Jim and she went off for a fortnight in the summer to Kerry or Connemara. It took Mrs Clery a full year to get used to it, and all that time she watched Eileen closely, expecting her each week to show signs of pregnancy. Perhaps it was fortunate that there were none. Heaven alone knows what she might have done.

Then Mrs Grahame fell ill, and Jim nursed her by day while Eileen took over from him at night. She was dying, and in the intervals of consciousness, she moulded Eileen's hands with her own and said: 'I always wanted a daughter, and I had my wish. I had my wish. Ye'll be happy now that ye have the house to yerselves. You'll look after Jim for me?'

'I'll look after him for you,' Eileen said, and on the night when his mother died she let him sleep on.

'I thought I'd better not wake you, Jim,' she said when she roused him next morning. 'You were so tired and Mammy went so peacefully ... That's the way she'd have wished it, Jim,' she added gravely when she saw his look of surprise.

'I dare say you're right, Eileen,' he agreed.

But their troubles were far from being at an end. When they proposed to shift into Jim's house, Mrs Clery raised more of a hullabaloo than she had raised over the marriage.

'Is it up among strangers?' she cried aghast.

'Strangers half a mile away, Mammy?' Eileen exclaimed, still unable to conceal a laugh at her mother's extraordinary reception of every new proposal.

'Half a mile?' her mother echoed dully. ' 'Tis a mile.'

'And you think your old friends would desert you?' asked Eileen.

'I wouldn't ask them,' her mother replied with dignity. 'I couldn't sleep in a place where I wouldn't hear the sound of the trams. Jim's mother died in her own house. Oh, my, isn't it a queer thing he wouldn't let me die in mine!'

And once more Jim and Eileen had to resign themselves to frustration. They could offer no adequate substitute for the soothing squeak of the trams climbing Summerhill from the city, and as Eileen saw, it would be folly for them to give up Jim's excellent house, which they would need later on, and come to share her own tiny cottage with a cranky mother-in-law.

Instead, they played at being married. On a couple of evenings each week, Eileen would give her mother supper early, and then come to Jim's house and have supper ready for him when he got in from the shop. When she heard his key in the lock, she ran to the front door to meet him in her white housecoat, and he would let on to be suitably astonished at seeing her. As they went in, she would point silently to the big fire she had lit in the living-room, and they would have supper together and read or talk till he saw her home coming on to midnight. Yet, even with the extra work, it gave them both a deep pleasure to make the big bed that Eileen never slept in except as a visitor, to wash up together, or, best of all, to entertain some friends, just as though Eileen did not, like Cinderella, have to fly back at midnight to her old part as daughter and nurse. Some day, they felt, the house would really be theirs, and she would open the door in the morning to milkman and breadman.

But this was not how things happened. Instead, Jim fell seriously ill, and rather than consent to the conflict which he knew this would set up in Eileen's mind between her duty to him and her duty to her mother, he chose to go to hospital. Two years after his mother's death, he died there.

Something seemed to happen to Eileen at this point that made even her mother afraid. There was no argument between them as to what she should do. She shut up her own cottage and her mother joined her in Jim's house where she received his relatives. The body had been taken to the church, and when Jim's family came, Eileen had lunch ready for them, and chatted as she served, as though the trouble had been theirs rather than hers. It was a cold lunch, and she was full of apologies. At the graveside while they wept, she showed no sign of tears. When the grave had been covered over Jim and his mother, she stood there silently, her head bowed, and Jim's aunt, an enormous woman, came up and took her two hands.

'You're a great little girl,' she whispered huskily. ' 'Twon't be forgotten for you.'

'But, Auntie,' Eileen replied, 'that's the way Jim would have liked it. It makes me feel close to him, and it won't be long till we're together again. Once Mammy goes, there'll be nothing to keep me.'

There was something about her words, and her dry-eyed air and her still-youthful face that the other woman found disconcerting.

'Ah, nonsense, child!' she said lightly. 'We all feel that way. You'll be happy yet, and you'll deserve it. One of these days you'll have a houseful of your own.'

'Oh, no, Auntie,' Eileen replied with a sweet smile that was curiously knowledgeable and even condescending, as though Jim's aunt were too much of a child to understand. 'You know yourself I could never find another husband like Jim. People can't be as happy as that a second time, you know. That would be too much to ask.'

And relatives and even neighbours began to realize that Eileen was only telling the truth; that in spite of everything she had been intensely happy, happy in some way they could not understand, and that what had seemed to them a mockery of marriage had indeed been one so complete and satisfying that beside it, even by their standards, a woman might think everything else in the world a mere shadow.

Rudyard Kipling

Georgie Porgie

> Georgie Porgie, pudding and pie,
> Kissed the girls and made them cry.
> When the girls came out to play
> Georgie Porgie ran away.

If you will admit that a man has no right to enter his drawing-room early in the morning, when the housemaid is setting things right and clearing away the dust, you will concede that civilized people who eat out of China and own card-cases have no right to apply their standard of right and wrong to an unsettled land. When the place is made fit for their reception, by those men who are told off to the work, they can come up, bringing in their trunks their own society and the Decalogue, and all the other apparatus. Where the Queen's Law does not carry, it is irrational to expect an observance of other and weaker rules. The men who run ahead of the cars of Decency and Propriety, and make the jungle ways straight, cannot be judged in the same manner as the stay-at-home folk of the ranks of the regular *Tchin.*

Not many months ago the Queen's Law stopped a few miles north of Thayetmyo on the Irrawaddy. There was no very strong Public Opinion up to that limit, but it existed to keep men in order. When the Government said that the Queen's Law must carry up to Bhamo and the Chinese border the order was given, and some men whose desire was to be ever a little in advance of the rush of Respectability flocked forward with the troops. These were the men who could never pass examinations, and would have been too pronounced in their ideas for the administration of bureau-worked Provinces. The Supreme Government stepped in as soon as might be, with codes and regulations, and all but reduced New Burma to the dead Indian level; but there was a short time during which strong men were necessary and ploughed a field for themselves.

Among the forerunners of Civilization was Georgie Porgie, reckoned by all who knew him a strong man. He held an appointment in Lower Burma when the order came to break the Frontier, and

his friends called him Georgie Porgie because of the singularly Bur-
mese-like manner in which he sang a song whose first line is something like the words 'Georgie Porgie'. Most men who have been
in Burma will know the song. It means: 'Puff, puff, puff, puff, great
steamboat!' Georgie sang it to his banjo, and his friends shouted
with delight, so that you could hear them far away in the teak-
forest.

When Georgie Porgie went to Upper Burma he had no special
regard for God or Man, but he knew how to make himself
respected, and to carry out the mixed Military-Civil duties that
fell to most men's share in those months. He did his office work
and entertained, now and again, the detachments of fever-shaken
soldiers who blundered through his part of the world in search of
a flying party of dacoits. Sometimes he turned out and dressed
down dacoits on his own account; for the country was still
smouldering and would blaze when least expected. He enjoyed
these charivaris, but the dacoits were not so amused. All the
officials who came in contact with him departed with the idea that
Georgie Porgie was a valuable person, well able to take care of
himself, and, on that belief, he was left to his own devices.

At the end of a few months he wearied of his solitude, and cast
about for company and refinement. The Queen's Law had hardly
begun to be felt in the country, and Public Opinion, which is more
powerful than the Queen's Law, had yet to come. Also, there was
a custom in the country which allowed a white man to take to
himself a wife of the Daughters of Heth upon due payment. The
marriage was not quite so binding as is the *nikkah* ceremony among
Mahomedans, but the wife was very pleasant.

When all our troops are back from Burma there will be a proverb
in their mouths, 'As thrifty as a Burmese wife,' and pretty English
ladies will wonder what in the world it means.

The headman of the village next to Georgie Porgie's post had
a fair daughter who had seen Georgie Porgie and loved him from
afar. When news went abroad that the Englishman with the heavy
hand who lived in the stockade was looking for a housekeeper, the
headman came in and explained that, for five hundred rupees
down, he would entrust his daughter to Georgie Porgie's keeping,
to be maintained in all honour, respect, and comfort, with pretty
dresses, according to the custom of the country. This thing was
done, and Georgie Porgie never repented it.

He found his rough-and-tumble house put straight and made

comfortable, his hitherto unchecked expenses cut down by one-half, and himself petted and made much of by his new acquisition, who sat at the head of his table and sang songs to him and ordered his Madrassee servants about, and was in every way as sweet and merry and honest and winning a little woman as the most exacting of bachelors could have desired. No race, men say who know, produces such good wives and heads of households as the Burmese. When the next detachment tramped by on the war-path the Subaltern in command found at Georgie Porgie's table a hostess to be deferential to, a woman to be treated in every way as one occupying an assured position. When he gathered his men together next dawn and replunged into the jungle he thought regretfully of the nice little dinner and the pretty face, and envied Georgie Porgie from the bottom of his heart. Yet *he* was engaged to a girl at Home, and that is how some men are constructed.

The Burmese girl's name was not a pretty one; but as she was promptly christened Georgina by Georgie Porgie, the blemish did not matter. Georgie Porgie thought well of the petting and the general comfort, and vowed that he had never spent five hundred rupees to a better end.

After three months of domestic life a great idea struck him. Matrimony—English matrimony—could not be such a bad thing after all. If he were so thoroughly comfortable at the Back of Beyond with this Burmese girl who smoked cheroots, how much more comfortable would he be with a sweet English maiden who would not smoke cheroots, and would play upon a piano instead of a banjo? Also he had a desire to return to his kind, to hear a Band once more, and to feel how it felt to wear a dress-suit again. Decidedly, Matrimony would be a very good thing. He thought the matter out at length of evenings, while Georgina sang to him, or asked him why he was so silent, and whether she had done anything to offend him. As he thought, he smoked, and as he smoked he looked at Georgina, and in his fancy turned her into a fair, thrifty, amusing, merry, little English girl, with hair coming low down on her forehead, and perhaps a cigarette between her lips. Certainly, not a big, thick, Burma cheroot, of the brand that Georgina smoked. He would wed a girl with Georgina's eyes and most of her ways. But not all. She could be improved upon. Then he blew thick smoke-wreaths through his nostrils and stretched himself. He would taste marriage. Georgina had helped him to save money, and there were six months' leave due to him.

'See here, little woman,' he said, 'we must put by more money for these next three months. I want it.' That was a direct slur on Georgina's housekeeping; for she prided herself on her thrift; but since her God wanted money she would do her best.

'You want money?' she said with a little laugh. 'I *have* money. Look!' She ran to her own room and fetched out a small bag of rupees. 'Of all that you give me, I keep back some. See! One hundred and seven rupees. Can you want more money than that? Take it. It is my pleasure if you use it.' She spread out the money on the table and pushed it towards him with her quick, little, pale yellow fingers.

Georgie Porgie never referred to economy in the household again.

Three months later, after the dispatch and receipt of several mysterious letters which Georgina could not understand, and hated for that reason, Georgie Porgie said that he was going away, and she must return to her father's house and stay there.

Georgina wept. She would go with her God from the world's end to the world's end. Why should she leave him? She loved him.

'I am only going to Rangoon,' said Georgie Porgie. 'I shall be back in a month, but it is safer to stay with your father. I will leave you two hundred rupees.'

'If you go for a month, what need of two hundred? Fifty are more than enough. There is some evil here. Do not go, or at least let me go with you.'

Georgie Porgie does not like to remember that scene even at this date. In the end he got rid of Georgina by a compromise of seventy-five rupees. She would not take more. Then he went by steamer and rail to Rangoon.

The mysterious letters had granted him six months' leave. The actual flight and an idea that he might have been treacherous hurt severely at the time, but as soon as the big steamer was well out into the blue, things were easier, and Georgina's face, and the queer little stockaded house, and the memory of the rushes of shouting dacoits by night, the cry and struggle of the first man that he had ever killed with his own hand, and a hundred other more intimate things, faded and faded out of Georgie Porgie's heart, and the vision of approaching England took its place. The steamer was full of men on leave, all rampantly jovial souls who had shaken off the dust and sweat of Upper Burma and were as merry as school-boys. They helped Georgie Porgie to forget.

Then came England with its luxuries and decencies and comforts, and Georgie Porgie walked in a pleasant dream upon pavements of which he had nearly forgotten the ring, wondering why men in their senses ever left Town. He accepted his keen delight in his furlough as the reward of his services. Providence further arranged for him another and greater delight—all the pleasures of a quiet English wooing, quite different from the brazen businesses of the East, when half the community stand back and bet on the result, and the other half wonder what Mrs So-and-So will say to it.

It was a pleasant girl and a perfect summer, and a big country-house near Petworth where there are acres and acres of purple heather and high-grassed water-meadows to wander through. Georgie Porgie felt that he had at last found something worth the living for, and naturally assumed that the next thing to do was to ask the girl to share his life in India. She, in her ignorance, was willing to go. On this occasion there was no bartering with a village headman. There was a fine middle-class wedding in the country, with a stout Papa and a weeping Mamma, and a best-man in purple and fine linen, and six snub-nosed girls from the Sunday School to throw roses on the path between the tombstones up to the Church door. The local paper described the affair at great length, even down to giving the hymns in full. But that was because the Direction were starving for want of material.

Then came a honeymoon at Arundel, and the Mamma wept copiously before she allowed her one daughter to sail away to India under the care of Georgie Porgie the Bridegroom. Beyond any question, Georgie Porgie was immensely fond of his wife, and she was devoted to him as the best and greatest man in the world. When he reported himself at Bombay he felt justified in demanding a good station for his wife's sake; and, because he had made a little mark in Burma and was beginning to be appreciated, they allowed him nearly all that he asked for, and posted him to a station which we will call Sutrain. It stood upon several hills, and was styled officially a 'Sanitarium', for the good reason that the drainage was utterly neglected. Here Georgie Porgie settled down, and found married life come very naturally to him. He did not rave, as do many bridegrooms, over the strangeness and delight of seeing his own true love sitting down to breakfast with him every morning 'as though it were the most natural thing in the world'. 'He had been there before,' as the Americans say, and, checking the merits of his own present Grace by those of Georgina, he was more and more inclined to think that he had done well.

But there was no peace or comfort across the Bay of Bengal, under the teak-trees where Georgina lived with her father, waiting for Georgie Porgie to return. The headman was old, and remembered the war of '51. He had been to Rangoon, and knew something of the ways of the *Kullahs*. Sitting in front of his door in the evenings, he taught Georgina a dry philosophy which did not console her in the least.

The trouble was that she loved Georgie Porgie just as much as the French girl in the English History books loved the priest whose head was broken by the King's bullies. One day she disappeared from the village, with all the rupees that Georgie Porgie had given her, and a very small smattering of English—also gained from Georgie Porgie.

The headman was angry at first, but lit a fresh cheroot and said something uncomplimentary about the sex in general. Georgina had started on a search for Georgie Porgie, who might be in Rangoon, or across the Black Water, or dead, for aught that she knew. Chance favoured her. An old Sikh policeman told her that Georgie Porgie had crossed the Black Water. She took a steerage-passage from Rangoon and went to Calcutta, keeping the secret of her search to herself.

In India every trace of her was lost for six weeks, and no one knows what trouble of heart she must have undergone.

She reappeared, four hundred miles north of Calcutta, steadily heading northwards, very worn and haggard, but very fixed in her determination to find Georgie Porgie. She could not understand the language of the people; but India is infinitely charitable, and the women-folk along the Grand Trunk gave her food. Something made her believe that Georgie Porgie was to be found at the end of that pitiless road. She may have seen a sepoy who knew him in Burma, but of this no one can be certain. At last, she found a regiment on the line of march, and met there one of the many subalterns whom Georgie Porgie had invited to dinner in the far off, old days of the dacoit-hunting. There was a certain amount of amusement among the tents when Georgina threw herself at the man's feet and began to cry. There was no amusement when her story was told; but a collection was made, and that was more to the point. One of the subalterns knew of Georgie Porgie's where-abouts, but not of his marriage. So he told Georgina and she went her way joyfully to the north, in a railway carriage where there was rest for tired feet and shade for a dusty little head. The marches from the train through the hills into Sutrain were trying, but Georgina had money, and families journeying in bullock-carts gave her help. It was an almost miraculous journey, and Georgina felt sure that the good spirits of Burma were looking after her. The hill-road to Sutrain is a chilly stretch, and Georgina caught a bad cold. Still there was Georgie Porgie at the end of all the trouble to take her up in his arms and pet her, as he used to do in the old days when the stockade was shut for the night and he had approved of the evening meal. Georgina went forward as fast as she could; and her good spirits did her one last favour.

An Englishman stopped her, in the twilight, just at the turn of the road in Sutrain, saying, 'Good Heavens! What are you doing here?'

He was Gillis, the man who had been Georgie Porgie's assistant in Upper Burma, and who occupied the next post to Georgie Porgie's in the jungle. Georgie Porgie had applied to have him to work with at Sutrain because he liked him.

'I have come,' said Georgina simply. 'It was such a long way, and I have been months in coming. Where is his house?'

Gillis gasped. He had seen enough of Georgina in the old times to know that explanations would be useless. You cannot explain things to the Oriental. You must show.

'I'll take you there,' said Gillis, and he led Georgina off the road, up the cliff, by a little pathway, to the back of a house set on a platform cut into the hillside.

The lamps were just lit, but the curtains were not drawn. 'Now look,' said Gillis, stopping in front of the drawing-room window. Georgina looked and saw Georgie Porgie and the Bride.

She put her hand up to her hair, which had come out of its top-knot and was straggling about her face. She tried to set her ragged dress in order, but the dress was past pulling straight, and she coughed a queer little cough, for she really had taken a very bad cold. Gillis looked, too, but while Georgina only looked at the Bride once, turning her eyes always on Georgie Porgie, Gillis looked at the Bride all the time.

'What are you going to do?' said Gillis, who held Georgina by the wrist, in case of any unexpected rush into the lamplight. 'Will you go in and tell that English woman that you lived with her husband?'

'No,' said Georgina faintly. 'Let me go. I am going away. I swear that I am going away.' She twisted herself free and ran off into the dark.

'Poor little beast!' said Gillis, dropping on to the main road. 'I'd ha' given her something to get back to Burma with. What a narrow shave though! And that angel would never have forgiven it.'

This seems to prove that the devotion of Gillis was not entirely due to his affection for Georgie Porgie.

The Bride and the Bridegroom came out into the verandah after dinner, in order that the smoke of Georgie Porgie's cheroots might not hang in the new drawing-room curtains.

'What is that noise down there?' said the Bride. Both listened.

'Oh,' said Georgie Porgie, 'I suppose some brute of a hillman has been beating his wife.'

'Beating—his—wife! How ghastly!' said the Bride. 'Fancy *your* beating *me*!' She slipped an arm round her husband's waist, and, leaning her head against his shoulder, looked out across the cloud-filled valley in deep content and security.

But it was Georgina crying, all by herself, down the hillside, among the stones of the watercourse where the washermen wash the clothes.

Sources and Acknowledgements

The editor wishes to thank the following authors (or their agents or trustees) and publishers who have granted permission to reproduce copyright material:

'The Coll Doll' by Walter Macken, from *The Coll Doll and Other Stories* (Macmillan, London and Basingstoke).

'A Question of Background' by Phyllis Bently, from *Tales of the West Riding* (Gollancz).

'Spiv in Love' by Bill Naughton.

'Advice to the Lovelorn' by Christopher Morley, from *Tales from a Rolltop Desk* © 1921 by Doubleday Page & Co. Copyright renewed 1949 by Christopher Morley. Reprinted by permission of J. B. Lippincott Company.

'The Fury' by Stan Barstow, from *The Desperados* (Michael Joseph).

'George Lambert and Miss P.' by Margery Sharp, from *The Lost Chapel Picnic and Other Stories* (William Heinemann).

'Too Early Spring', from *Selected Works of Stephen Vincent Benet* (Holt, Rinehart and Winston Inc.) © 1937 Stephen Vincent Benet, copyright renewed 1964 Thomas C. Benet, Stephine B. Mahin and Rachel Benet Lewis. Reprinted by permission of Brandt and Brandt.

'A Taste of Blood' by H. E. Bates, from *The Yellow Meads of Asphodel* (Michael Joseph) by permission of Laurence Pollinger and the Estate of the late H. E. Bates.

'The End of Something' by Ernest Hemingway, from *The First Forty-Nine Stories* (Jonathan Cape) and from *In Our Time* (Charles Scribner's Sons) © 1925 Charles Scribner's Sons, by permission of the executors of Ernest Hemingway estate.

'The Impossible Marriage' by Frank O'Connor, from *Collection Three* (Macmillan, London and Basingstoke) by permission of A. D. Peters.

'Georgie Porgie' by Rudyard Kipling, from *Life's Handicap* (Macmillan, London and Basingstoke) by permission of the National Trust.